Land Invertebrates

Land Invertebrates

A GUIDE TO BRITISH WORMS, MOLLUSCS
AND ARTHROPODS (EXCLUDING INSECTS)

J. L. CLOUDSLEY-THOMPSON
Professor of Zoology
University of Khartoum, Sudan

and

JOHN SANKEY
Warden, Juniper Hall Field Centre
(Field Studies Council), Dorking, Surrey

METHUEN & CO LTD
11 NEW FETTER LANE EC4

First published in 1961
Reprinted 1968
© *1961 by J. L. Cloudsley-Thompson & John Sankey*
Printed in Great Britain by
Butler & Tanner Ltd, Frome & London
S.B.N. 416 64020 6
I.2

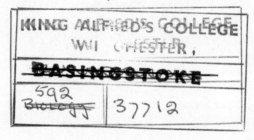
Distributed in the U.S.A.
by Barnes & Noble, Inc.

You only need sit still long enough in some attractive spot in the woods that all its inhabitants may exhibit themselves to you by turns.

Henry David Thoreau (1817–62)
in
A BATTLE OF ANTS

ACKNOWLEDGMENTS

In writing a book of this kind, we have naturally had to draw heavily on the knowledge and skill of others. It is our privilege and pleasure to acknowledge their help. We are especially indebted to Miss Ann Hitch who prepared many of the figures, to Dr G. Inglis for assistance with the chapter on roundworms, to Dr Betty Roots for her help and advice on earthworms, to Dr C. A. Edwards for helping over the symphylids and pauropods, to Dr G. Owen Evans who gave us invaluable assistance with the presentation of the section on mites and ticks, and to Dr H. E. Quick who kindly advised us on slugs and snails. Mr Gordon Blower read the chapters on woodlice, millipedes and centipedes and gave us the benefit of his wide experience, while Professor C. F. A. Pantin, F.R.S., and Mr S. Prudhoe kindly advised us on matters concerned with Chapter 2. Mrs Cecily Morrison and Miss Dilys Thomas typed the manuscript and provided valuable editorial assistance. The sources of figures re-drawn from the works of others are acknowledged in the appropriate legends. For the inevitable errors and shortcomings of the book, we are, of course, entirely responsible.

J. L. C.-T.
J. S.

January 1960

CONTENTS

9

ILLUSTRATIONS

14

Chapter One

INTRODUCTION

Naturalists are most fortunate people because, wherever they go and whatever they do, there is always something to interest them. But, just as a little knowledge is essential for a true appreciation and enjoyment of music and the arts, so an aimless love of natural history does not really satisfy our innate desire to understand nature. The more enthusiasm and effort that we devote to a subject, the greater and more lasting is the satisfaction that it yields.

The best way to acquire a wider knowledge of animals in general is first to specialise on a particular group or groups. Thus, not only do we learn a number of important principles, but having something definite to look for makes us more observant generally. Moreover, it might as well be recognised at the outset that a dilettante interest is not really satisfactory. In order to achieve any success, the difficult problem of identification must sometime be faced.

The correct identification of animals is an art which needs practice. Some kinds, such as butterflies and birds, give little difficulty and, indeed, can often be recognised at a glance. Others may be extremely difficult, and the student must be prepared to devote hours of hard and often frustrating labour at the outset when faced with particularly intractable specimens. It is to simplify problems of this kind and to help in the identification of the more common, yet little known invertebrate animals of Britain's woods and fields that this book has been written.

Identification depends very much on what is meant by a

'species'. Biologists are by no means fully agreed upon a suitable definition and the precise meaning of the term has been the subject of much discussion. The late Dr W. T. Calman defined a species as: 'an assemblage of animals which do not differ from one another more than the offspring of a single pair may do; which are not connected with the members of neighbouring assemblages by intermediate forms; which interbreed freely with one another but commonly do not (in the wild state) interbreed with other species, or, if they do, produce infertile hybrids; and which usually inhabit geographical areas distinct from those inhabited by the most nearly related species'. Where possible we have tried to give specific descriptions, but certain difficult, or 'specialist', groups of animals have not been taken beyond the order, sub-order, family or genus.

If one knows the probable answer to a problem, its solution is naturally much simplified. Much unrewarding labour in identification can be saved if one knows what to expect. For example, no less than 38 species of woodlice are known to occur in the British Isles, but of these, only eight are really common. Unless one of the rare or local species is deliberately sought for, any woodlouse collected at random in the field is almost certain to be one of the eight. We have therefore attempted not only to give adequate descriptions for the precise identification of these, as well as one or two others that may occasionally turn up, but to make our diagnoses sufficiently detailed for the reader to realise when, by chance, he has collected one of the rare forms. In that case, of course, reference must be made to one of the monographic works listed in the references.

The value of making one's own collections and consulting those in museums cannot be over-emphasised. Identification is often made easier and quicker by the use of keys and we have used these where necessary. Where two or more alternative characters or groups of characters are given, *all* should be read in sequence. Comparative characters sometimes arise, and in such cases only experience or the use of a type collection can help. If doubt exists in following a key, it is best to try one alternative and if the specimen does not 'key out', the other character must be the correct one. It should always be remembered that a key is intended as a *guide* to identification, and that specimens should be checked against a fuller description whenever possible.

Since perhaps five or six times as many adult and larval insects will be caught as of every other kind of invertebrate animal, it is well to be able to recognise an insect when we find one. The body of an insect is divided into three parts; the head, thorax and abdomen. The head bears a pair of feelers or antennae, and attached to the thorax are three pairs of legs and, often, wings. This definition may seem clear enough and, in so far as it applies to *adults*, it is sound. But no general definition will cover the diversity of immature forms; caterpillars, maggots, the various exopterygote nymphs (larvae of insects with only three stages in their life-cycle) and so on. Many of these show no separation of the body into thorax and abdomen, and others possess abdominal as well as thoracic legs. Some stages are without head or antennae, others are without legs at all. We therefore append a page illustrating a selection of insect types (p. 20). With a little experience, the beginner will soon learn to distinguish insects from other kinds of land invertebrates. For further information about them, he is advised to consult one of the many reliable entomological text-books already in existence. Information about particular groups and other aspects of the British insect fauna is available in Messrs Collin's excellent *New Naturalist Series* and in Warne's *Wayside and Woodlands Series*, and in the *Handbooks for the Identification of British Insects* published by the Royal Entomological Society of London. A general introduction to the class is given by Imms, A. D. (1959), *Outlines of Entomology*, London, Methuen; Moreton, B. D. (1958), *Guide to British Insects*,

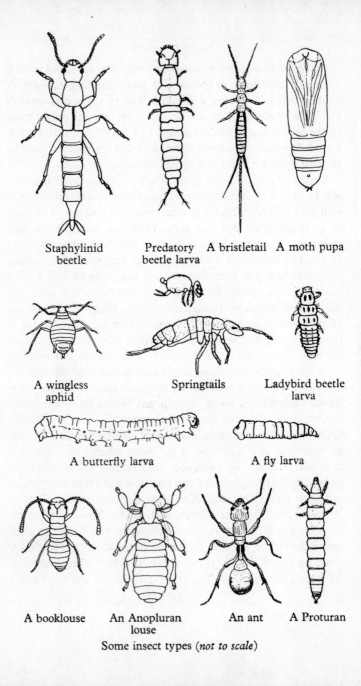

Staphylinid
beetle

Predatory
beetle larva

A bristletail

A moth pupa

A wingless
aphid

Springtails

Ladybird beetle
larva

A butterfly larva

A fly larva

A booklouse

An Anopluran
louse

An ant

A Proturan

Some insect types (*not to scale*)

London, Macmillan; Skidmore, P. (1958), *British Insects – a simplified key to the orders*, Manchester, Flatters and Garnett, are also recommended. In view of the amount of information already available, insects are excluded from the present volume. So, too, are *Collembola* or Springtails (see p. 79), internal parasites and aquatic animals.

Identification is easier with good specimens and full notes. Collection in the field with the right apparatus and careful noting of the habitat, e.g. food plant, kind of soil, etc., are therefore essential. The most useful apparatus possessed by any naturalist in the field is a sharp pair of eyes! Collection and preservation methods are given by Adams (1959), Bayliss & Monro (1941), Sankey (1959) and Wagstaff & Fidler (1957). May we remind collectors that a good hand-lens and a notebook should always be taken into the field.

We have tried, as far as possible, to produce a book which can be used in the field by beginners, and have therefore selected the more conspicuous diagnostic features of the various genera and species. From our experience in teaching practical ecology over a number of years, we believe that there is need of a book that will guide the student through the bewildering profusion of species that tends to make more advanced works so overwhelming. It is our hope that the present volume, by relieving some of the tedium of systematic identification, will enable sixth-form and first-year university students, as well as amateur natural history workers throughout the country, to enjoy more fully the intellectual delights of field work.

REFERENCES

ADAMS, C. V. A. (1959) *Nature is my hobby*. Exeter: Wheaton.

BAYLISS, H. A., and MONRO, C. C. A. (1941) *Instructions for collectors*, No. 9a. London: British Museum (Natural History).

SANKEY, J. (1959) *Guide to field biology*. London: Longmans.

WAGSTAFFE, R., and FIDLER, J. H. (1957) *The preservation of natural history specimens*, I. *Invertebrates*. London: Witherby.

KEY TO LAND INVERTEBRATES OTHER THAN INSECTS

1. With locomotory limbs 2
   Without locomotory limbs 8

2. Body broad and flat, seven pairs of legs[1]
                      ISOPODA (Woodlice, p. 48)
   Body elongate with many segments, more than four pairs
   of legs 3
   With four pairs of legs 6
   [Insects, which have three pairs of thoracic legs, are
   not included in this book. See p. 20]

3. Body very elongate 4
   Body less elongate, very small animals . . . 5

4. Typical body segments (in middle) each with one pair
   of legs . . CHILOPODA (Centipedes, p. 70)
   Typical body segments with two pairs of legs, coil up
   into a 'watch-spring' when disturbed
                      DIPLOPODA (Millipedes, p. 60)

5. With nine pairs of legs and branched antennae
                      PAUROPODA (p. 79)
   With twelve pairs of legs . . SYMPHYLA (p. 81)

[1] The pill-millipede, *Glomeris* (p. 62) has 17 pairs of legs.

6. Small scorpion-like animals with very large 'lobster claw' chelae on palps (figs. 90–107)

    CHELONETHI (False-scorpions, p. 84)

    Not as above 7

7. Body apparently in two parts, eyes 6 or 8, second legs not the longest; produce silk from abdominal spinnerets. . . . ARANEAE (Spiders, p. 101)

    Body not in two distinct parts, eyes 2, second legs the longest; no silk glands

    OPILIONES (Harvest-spiders, p. 92)

    Small animals with rarely any traces of external segmentation; front part of cephalothorax produced into a well-marked 'capitulum' (fig. 169) ACARI (Mites, p. 122)

8. With two pairs of tentacles and no obvious external segmentation, some with a shell

    MOLLUSCA (Slugs and snails, p. 131)

    No tentacles 9

9. Body large (except white-worms, p. 37), rounded, and with well-marked segments

    OLIGOCHAETA (Earthworms, p. 37)

    Body very long and thin, with no segmentation

    NEMERTINI (p. 25)

    NEMATODA (Roundworms) (p. 26)

    NEMATOMORPHA (Threadworms) (p. 35)

    Body distinctly flattened, not very long and thin

    TRICLADIDA (Planarians, p. 24)

Chapter Two

FLATWORMS AND ROUNDWORMS

TRICLADIDA, METANEMERTINI, NEMATODA AND NEMATOMORPHA

The systematic position of some of the groups of animals dealt with in this chapter is not yet finally settled, and in all there is more than ample scope for observations on their general biology and ecology.

Two phyla are involved:

(1) Platyhelminthes

Class Turbellaria (flatworms)
  Order Tricladida, genera – *Microplana* and *Rhynchodemus* (land planarians)
Class Nemertini (Nemertines)
  Order Metanemertini, genus *Geonemertes*

(2) Aschelminthes

Class Nematoda (round- or eelworms)
Class Nematomorpha (hair- or threadworms), genera – *Gordius* and *Parachordodes*

Land planarians

Small flattish and somewhat slimy-looking animals which move slowly over damp stones or pieces of wood on rich soils in shady moist habitats. They fragment very readily and are best put quickly into 70% alcohol by means of a small soft brush.

There are four British species:

Microplana (= *Orthodemus*) *terrestris* (O. F. Müller). Maximum length about 26 mm. Body light grey to darkish grey-brown, evenly cylindrical; eyes minute. Genital pore ventral, slightly in front of mid-point of body; mouth just in front of this point. Common and widely distributed though not usually recorded.

M. (= *Orthodemus*) *britannicus* Percival. Maximum length about 90 mm. May contract to one-sixth of its length. Colour salmon pink, sulphur yellow or dirty grey. Mouth ventral about half-way down body; genital pore about 5–8 mm. behind mouth. Rarely recorded: Cheshire, Devonshire, Yorkshire.

M. (= *Orthodemus*) *scharffi* von Graff. Maximum length about 45 mm. Colour bright yellow. Mouth placed about threequarters of body length from anterior end. Genital pore 2–2·5 mm. behind mouth. Recorded only from Ireland but would be worth searching for elsewhere. It may prove to be conspecific with *M. britannicus*.

Rhynchodemus bilineatus (Mecznikow) (fig. 1). Up to about 8 mm. long. Colour variable, light to dark. Head dark above, pale below; eyes large, just behind snout. Anterior region flattened with a cephalic groove ventrally; the whole of the front part sways from side to side in the living animal. Rest of body with two long dorsal stripes and a median dark area above pharynx. Ventral surface dirty white except for about six brown spots which are joined by fine lines of pigment; spots often circular. Cambridge, Cornwall, Devonshire.

Nemertines

The only member of this curious group of animals is *Geonemertes dendyi* Dakin (fig. 2). It is similar in appearance to the planarian *Microplana terrestris* (see above). Its size is variable and it may attain a length of 25 mm. The colour is yellowish or lightish brown and there are two longitudinal darker dorsal stripes. There is a variable number of eyes placed laterally in groups of four. Its most characteristic feature when alive is the habit of everting its long proboscis when touched (fig. 3); the tip is placed on the substratum and the rest of the body is then drawn forwards over it so that it comes to rest in its original position inside the body. The animal's more normal progression is aided by copious

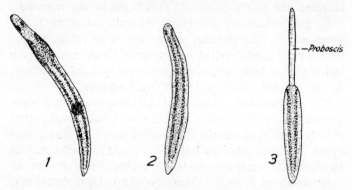

1. *Rhynchodemus bilineatus*   2 *Geonemertes*
3 *Geonemertes* with proboscis everted

amounts of slime. *G. dendyi* is said to suck the body juices of other animals. It appears to be an established alien from W. Australia, and it lives under stones and pieces of wood in damp and shady places near streams or trees in undisturbed areas. This species has been recorded from S. Devon, Swansea, Bangor, Wirral, New Forest and County Kerry.

Roundworms

Most free-living eelworms or Nematoda are less than 1·0 mm. long; they are small and thin (with few exceptions) and are barely visible to the naked eye. They should not be confused with white-worms, see p. 37. The majority of Nematodes have a cylindrical body, some females, however, are elongated anteriorly, swollen towards the posterior end, giving a sac-like appearance. The main diagnostic characters are:

(a) The shape of the mouth, which may be surrounded by three or six lips (sometimes fused or modified in various ways), with *papillae* arranged in two circles of sixes and one circle of four.

(b) The form of the genital organs. The *ovaries* or *testes* are paired or single. The former open into a common uterus through

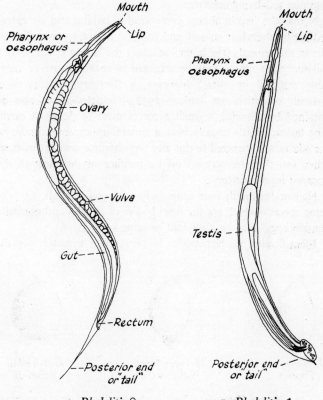

4. *Rhabditis* ♀   5. *Rhabditis* ♂

(After Borradaile, Potts, Eastham and Saunders, 1935)

which the fertilised eggs are passed to the exterior via the *vagina* and *vulva*, which opens on the ventral surface of the body. In the male there is a single *vas deferens*, situated ventrally, which opens posteriorly into the *rectum*. *Spicules* and special copulatory organs are usually present at the rear of the male body and are very useful in delimiting species. *Rhabditis* sp. (figs. 4 & 5) is a common soil-living eelworm.

Nematodes live in almost every kind of habitat and are extraordinarily abundant in soil and humus. Many are parasites of plants and animals (the latter including the largest species). The soil and plant species may be collected by soaking earth or vegetable material in water; however, a Baermann apparatus is virtually essential, see Sankey (1958). Nematodes can also be obtained by allowing a small piece of meat to decay in earth. The larvae, which usually bear a general appearance similar to the adults, are attracted to this and soon become sexually mature. They can then be scraped off the surface of the meat in the decayed liquid matter.

Nematodes moult four times before becoming adult. *Cysts* of some species (which are the dead bodies of females and normally contain eggs) may be abundant in some soils (fig. 6).

Identification of Nematodes is very much a matter for the

H. punctata Thorne	*H. rostochiensis* Wollenweber	*H. schachtii* Schmidt

6. Cysts of *Heterodera*. Each is about half the size of a pinhead

(After Southey, 1959)

specialist. A good microscope is essential for their study. They can be preserved in the following formula: 40% formalin 10 c.c., glacial acetic acid 10 c.c., water 80 c.c. For critical examination staining and mounting is necessary. Full details of this process are given in Goodey (1951), Wagstaffe & Fidler (1957), and Goodey, J. B. (1957). A useful publication dealing with various aspects of nematodology, including the principal genera of the plant parasites, has been edited by Southey (1959).

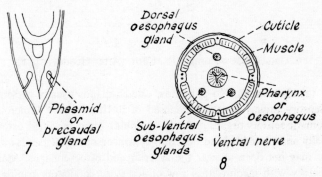

7. Precaudal glands (phasmids) of *Rhabditis* (after Goodey, 1951). 8. Section through the anterior end of a Phasmid eelworm to show the position of the sub-ventral oesophageal glands. (After Southey, 1959)

The Nematoda are divided into two sub-classes: (1) *Phasmidia.* Pre-caudal glands (*phasmids*) present (fig. 7). No *caudal glands.* Sensory organs on lips papilloid, rarely setose. *Amphids* (sensory organs) labial in position, pore-like. *Sub-ventral oesophageal* glands (fig. 8) not opening near anterior end of *oesophagus.* Male with no medioventral row of accessory copulatory organs and frequently with *caudal alae* (fig. 9). Many free-living forms; the majority of the animal and plant parasites belong to this subclass.

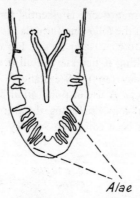

9. Caudal alae of a male *Rhabditis*. (After Goodey, 1951)

(2) *Aphasmidia*. No phasmids. Caudal glands usually present. Sensory organs usually composed of distinct setae. Numerous somatic sensory organs on body. Amphids often modified externally and placed behind lips. Sub-ventral oesophageal glands may or may not open at near the anterior end of oesophagus. Male usually with medioventral row of accessory copulatory papillae. Caudal alae rarely present. Many aquatic forms (some of which also live in damp places on land); some are animal parasites and a few are plant ectoparasites.

A useful key to the important orders is given by Jones *in* Southey (1959); there is also an abbreviated key to some families of the Tylenchida many of which are plant parasites and are often found in soil. We give here a slightly modified version of this key to the orders (this key only applies to forms occurring in soil and freshwater):

1. {
Free-living, in soil or freshwater, associated with or
parasitic on plants 2
Insect parasites 5

2. Amphids obscure, median and posterior oesophageal bulb usually present; no caudal gland or spinneret (a small protuberant terminal adhesive organ) absent. Male often with bursa but no median gential accessory copulatory apparatus 3

Amphids prominent, caudal glands and spinneret usually present. Male without bursa but often with median genital accessory copulatory apparatus . 4

3. Mouth spear present . . . . *Tylenchida*
Mouth spear absent . . . . *Rhabditida*

4. Amphids spiral or circular . . . *Chromadorida*
Amphids pouch-shaped . . . . . *Enoplida*

5. Body swollen when adult; uterus sometimes prolapsed, i.e. swollen and protuberant . *Tylenchida* Family Allantonematidae or superfam. *Aphelenchoidea*
Body vermiform 6

6. Oesophagus degenerate consisting of a long thin cuticular tube embedded in a glandular mass . *Enoplida*, Family Mermithidae
Oesophagus muscular 7

7. Mouth spear present. Oesophagus with median bulb *Tylenchida*
Mouth spear absent. Oesophagus with or without median bulb . . . . . *Rhabditida*

A good introductory account of the Nematoda is given in Kevan (1955) in which some of the more prominent genera are mentioned.

Amongst the Rhabditida the genera *Diplogaster* (figs. 10 & 11) and *Rhabditis* (figs. 4 & 5) are well represented in rotting vegetation. *Cephalobus* (figs. 12 & 13) species are typical soil forms.

31

10. *Diplogaster* anterior end

11. *Diplogaster* male tail

(Figs. 10–15 after Southey, 1959; figs. 16 and 17 after Goodey 1951)

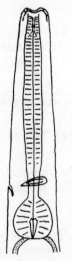

12. *Cephalobus* anterior end   13. *Cephalobus* male tail

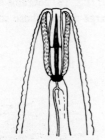

14. *Tylenchus* anterior end of female

15. *Tylenchus* male tail

16. *Aphelenchoides* female tail

17. *Aphelenchoides* male tail

C

In the Tylenchida, *Tylenchus* (figs. 14 & 15) contains soil-living species and the large genus *Aphelenchoides* (figs. 16 & 17) is composed of free-living forms as well as insect and plant parasites. The genus *Heterodera* contains important root parasitic species that are very injurious to crops; the cysts are often common in soil round the host plants and may be floated out in water (see fig. 6).

Amongst the Chromadorida, *Plectus* (fig. 18) contains soil and freshwater forms. *Monohystera* is a large genus whose members inhabit soil and freshwater (fig. 19).

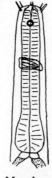

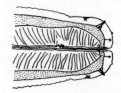

20. *Tripyla* anterior end of female, lateral view

18. *Plectus* male tail

19. *Monohystera* anterior end

(After Southey, 1959)

The Enoplida include a number of species which appear to inhabit both damp soil and freshwater as well as species found commonly in earth. Some species of *Tripyla* (fig. 20) may be carnivorous, feeding on other nematodes and rotifers. *Mononchus* (fig. 21) also contains a number of carnivorous species many of which live in earth. *Dorylaimus* spp. (fig. 22) are also earth and humus dwellers and some appear to inhabit both soil and freshwater. *Xiphenema*, which feeds on roots, has recently been shown

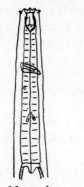 

21. *Mononchus*   22. *Dorylaimus*
anterior end   anterior end
(After Southey, 1959)

to transmit viruses. Species of the genus *Mermis* are between
40 and 200 mm. long and are parasitic in the young stages but
free-living when adult; the oesophagus ends blindly; the female
Mermis may be found crawling on plants after summer showers
in June and July in Britain; the males usually remain below
ground.

Hair- or Threadworms

Like Mermithid Nematodes (*Mermis*), these creatures may reach
an extraordinary length, sometimes up to 300 mm. or more. The
four British species (all within the family Gordiidae) vary in
colour from light brown to black, which distinguishes them from
the nematode genus *Mermis*. Their general appearance is that of
a piece of thick horse hair. The males are smaller and the tip of
their body is cleft. The alimentary canal is more or less
degenerate.

Hairworms occur in the neighbourhood of, or in, freshwater.
In the young stages they are parasitic in certain Arthropods,

35

especially insects. Goodey (1963) gives an account of the British species which can be distinguished by their skin patterns. These can be seen by clearing small pieces of skin in glycerine.

REFERENCES

GOODEY, T. (1963) *Soil and freshwater nematodes, 2nd ed.* London: Methuen.

GOODEY, J. B. (1957) *Laboratory methods for work with plant and soil nematodes,* Technical Bulletin No. 2. London: H.M.S.O.

KEVAN, D. K. McE. (Editor) (1955) *Soil zoology.* London: Butterworth.

SANKEY, J. (1958) *Guide to field biology.* London: Longmans.

SOUTHEY, J. F. (Editor) (1959) *Plant nematology,* Technical Bulletin No. 7. London: H.M.S.O.

WAGSTAFFE, R., and FIDLER, J. H. (1957) *The preservation of natural history specimens,* I. London: Witherby.

Chapter Three

EARTHWORMS

OLIGOCHAETA

The phylum Annelida comprises segmented worms with soft and usually elongated or cylindrical bodies. The skin is covered by a thin, protective cuticle and the segmentation of the body is shown externally by a series of rings extending from the front end to the tail of the animal. Of the various classes into which the phylum is sub-divided, only one, Oligochaeta, has terrestrial members: the others inhabit almost exclusively marine or freshwater habitats. Although a number of families belong to the class Oligochaeta, only two of them are terrestrial in Britain, the Lumbricidae and the Enchytraeidae, the remainder being freshwater or marine in habit.

Enchytraeid worms or 'white worms', sometimes called 'pot worms' (figs. 23 & 24), are small, rarely more than 25 mm. in length and usually white or pinkish in colour. They can be recognised by the fact that the *chaetae*, setae or bristles occur in bundles, of which there are usually four per segment. The Enchytraeidae may be extraordinarily abundant in damp places and large numbers can be observed by turning over the stones between tide-marks, in bogs and on the banks of rivers and lakes. Identification is extremely difficult and usually requires microscopic examination of serial sections of the body.

Earthworms of the family Lumbricidae (Fig. 25a) are typical inhabitants of the soil and most species have a wide distribution throughout the country. Populations of a million worms to the

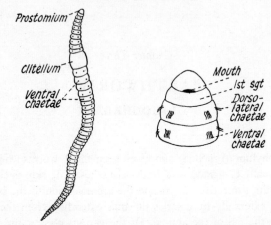

23. Enchytraeid worm   24. Head of Enchytraeid worm

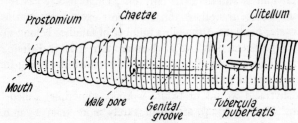

25a. Anterior end of earthworm showing features of
systematic importance

25b. Earthworm capsule

acre are by no means unusual, and as many as three million per
acre have been estimated for some permanent pastures. Especially
large numbers occur where the soil is rich in nitrogenous matter.
Inorganic fertilisers which encourage plant growth also encourage

38

earthworms, though cultivation will reduce the numbers of some species common in old grass land. Liming acid soil often increases the earthworm population.

Annelid worms move through the soil by forcing their anterior end into the crevices between soil particles and then expanding it so that the space is widened: if the soil is very compact, they eat a way through it. Some species, such as the well-known *Lumbricus terrestris,* inhabit U-shaped burrows from which the animal protrudes at night whilst it is feeding on leaves and other organic material. Worms are extremely sensitive to vibrations of the soil, so it is necessary to walk very quietly if their habits are to be observed. During the day the front of the burrow of *L. terrestris* is usually plugged with a tuft of leaves, sticks and stones. Burrowing activity increases greatly when food is scarce and considerable amounts of earth may then be swallowed and ejected after all the nutriment has been extracted. Only two species in this country, *Allolobophora longa* and *A. nocturna,* produce worm-casts to an appreciable degree on the surface; the majority of worms deposit their casts within the soil. *L. terrestris* produces some surface casts, but only in small amounts.

Water relations play an important part in the economy of earthworms which have a moist surface and no protection from desiccation. In times of drought many species retreat downwards to the moist sub-soil. Others survive unfavourable conditions by rolling themselves into a knot in a spherical earthen chamber lined with mucus. Not only can earthworms withstand very considerable water-loss, but many species are able to live under water provided that this is well oxygenated. Many live entirely in the water-logged mud of rivers and lakes, but these are not regarded as terrestrial animals in this volume.

Worms normally move away from light, and if forced to come to the surface after heavy rain, soon become paralysed by the ultra-violet so that they are unable to burrow and eventually die.

Although they are hermaphrodite, cross-fertilisation usually occurs. The eggs are deposited in the soil in capsules (fig. 25*b*). Although several eggs are contained in each capsule, only one worm eventually hatches, except in the case of *Eisenia foetida*, from the cocoons of which several young worms usually emerge. Worm cocoons may often be found in humus-rich soil and the more alkaline kinds of woodland litter; they are rarely more than 3–4 mm. long.

The ability to regenerate lost segments is much more limited than often thought, the capacity to develop a new head decreasing rapidly behind the ninth segment. For further biological details, the reader is referred to the excellent article by Roots (1956) or to the monograph by Stephenson (1930).

26. Epilobous prostomium
(dorsal view)

27. Tanylobous prostomium
(dorsal view)

The body in British species is usually cylindrical, tapering at both ends, the tail being often flattened dorso-ventrally. The length varies from about 17 mm. to 300 mm., the number of segments ranging from about 75 to 250 or more according to the species. The segment behind the mouth is counted as the first or *peristomium* and bears a head-lobe or *prostomium*. The mode of connection between the prostomium and peristomium is a diagnostic character and the prostomium may be *epilobous* or *tanylobous* (figs. 26 & 27), depending on whether the prostomium reaches back as far as the second segment when seen in dorsal view.

Each segment except the first and last bears eight chitinous and protrusible chaetae which assist in locomotion and mating. The distance between these is a systematic character and they may be closely or widely paired (fig. 33).

The main systematic characters, however, are the structure and position of the reproductive organs and immature specimens cannot usually be identified with certainty. Mature worms can easily be recognised by the presence of a glandular and often saddle-shaped girdle or *clitellum* in the anterior region of the body (fig. 25*a*). Its position and the number of segments it occupies provides an important diagnostic feature.

On the under side of the clitellum there is a pair of glandular swellings or *tubercula pubertatis* which may form continuous ridges over a number of segments or appear as separate papillae. These, too, are important in identification.

Earthworms may be preserved in 5% formalin, or in 70% alcohol or industrial methylated spirit, but this should be changed several times as it becomes diluted by the water contained in the bodies of the worms which soon disintegrate in weak solutions. Propylene phenoxetol may also be used (see p. 134). Identification requires careful examination with a lens or preferably a binocular microscope.

There are 25 species of the family Lumbricidae in the British Isles, but only *Lumbricus terrestris, Allolobophora longa, A. nocturna, Octolasium lacteum* and *O. cyaneum* reach a large size. The 12 most common terrestrial earthworms are described below. For the identification of others, the reader is referred to the monograph by Cernosvitov & Evans (1947).

Genus *Lumbricus*

Earthworms of this genus are reddish in colour and can be recognised by the fact that the prostomium is tanylobous (fig. 27) and the chaetae closely paired. (The presence of tubercula

pubertatis forming longitudinal ridges extending over four segments (fig. 28) distinguishes them from other species which have
a tanylobous prostomium. *Lumbricus* spp. should therefore not
be confused with *Bimastus eiseni* Levinsen an uncommon though
fairly widely distributed species from which tubercula pubertatis
are absent, or the rare *Eisenia veneta* Rosa in which there are only
two pairs.)

Lumbricus terrestris (L.). Length: 90–300 mm.; diameter:
6–9 mm.; segments: 110–160. This large, abundant and widely,
though sometimes locally, distributed earthworm can be recognised by its size and coloration. It has a reddish chestnut-brown
pigmentation dorsally, a yellowish ventral surface and a prominent orange-red clitellum. The body is cylindrical and when alive
a characteristic dorso-ventral flattening of the tail region can
often be observed. Clitellum, segments 31 or 32–37; tubercula
pubertatis, segments 33–36. Male pores conspicuous.

This purely terrestrial species lives in burrows 2–2½ m. deep
in pastures and forests, especially in clay soil. Unlike other
'large' species it is not adversely affected by cultivation, and is
thus quite common in gardens.

Lumbricus rubellus (Hoff.). Length: 60–150 mm.; diameter:
4–6 mm.; segments: 95–120. A smaller ruddy-brown species
often irridescent dorsally and ventrally pale yellow. The body is
cylindrical, the posterior end mostly flattened dorsally. Clitellum,
segments 26 or 27–32; tubercula pubertatis, segments 28–31.
This very common species, sometimes known as the Marsh
Worm, or Red Worm, occurs especially in damp places rich in
humus. It is abundant in parks, gardens, pastures, etc.

Lumbricus festivus (Sav.). Length: 48–105 mm.; diameter:
4·5–5 mm.; segments: 100–143. Ruddy-brown in colour, irridescent dorsally and lightly coloured ventrally. Clitellum prominent

on segments ½33 or 34–39. Tubercula pubertatis uniformly broad on segments 35–38. Male pores conspicuous.

Widely distributed in soil, under leaves and dung in pastures and meadows.

Lumbricus castaneus (Sav.). Length: 30–35 mm.; diameter: 3·5–4·5 mm.; segments: 82–100. Chestnut to violet-brown in

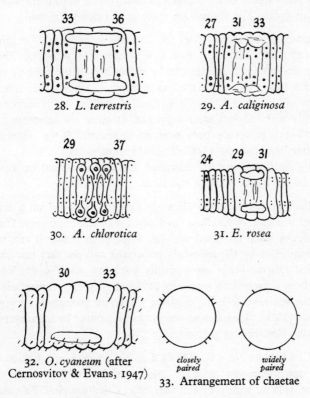

28. *L. terrestris*

29. *A. caliginosa*

30. *A. chlorotica*

31. *E. rosea*

32. *O. cyaneum* (after Cernosvitov & Evans, 1947)

closely paired   *widely paired*

33. Arrangement of chaetae

Tubercula pubertatis of earthworms

colour, strongly irridescent, and brownish-yellow ventrally. Clitellum orange, on segments 28–33, tubercula pubertatis of equal width on segments 29–32.

Widely distributed in rich and moist soil but less common than the rather similar but larger *L. rubellus*.

Genus *Allolobophora*

The prostomium is not tanylobous in any of the common species of this genus. The chaetae are more or less closely paired.

Allolobophora longa (Ude) (*A. terrestris* form *longa*). Length: 90–120 mm.; diameter: 6–9 mm.; segments: 160–200. This large and common species can be recognised in the field by its muddy-brown colour and the way in which it rushes to the surface if the soil in which it lives is vibrated. Clitellum not prominent, usually with distinct inter-segmental grooves, on segments 27 or 28–35; tubercula pubertatis on segments 32–34. Genital chaetae, segments 9–11 (cf. *Allolobophora nocturna*).

Widely distributed in cultivated soil and abundant in most soil on the banks of rivers and lakes.

Allolobophora nocturna (Evans). Length: 90–180 mm.; diameter in region of clitellum: 4–6 mm.; segments: 200–250. This species is often confused with *A. longa* from which it can be distinguished by the tubercula pubertatis and the fact that the genital chaetae occur on segments 9–12 instead of 9–11. The clitellum is present on segments $\frac{1}{2}$27 or 28–$\frac{1}{2}$35, the segmentation on the ventral side being distinct. Tubercula pubertatis on segments 31 and 33, extending over 32 but separated by a transverse furrow. Common in pastures.

Allolobophora chlorotica (Sav.). Length: 40–70 mm.; diameter: 4–5 mm.; segments: 80–125. Colour variable, various shades of green, yellow, pink, grey and slate blue. Clitellum pink. Pale and somewhat transparent so that yellow cells within the coelom can

44

EARTHWORMS

be seen moving up and down as in *A. caliginosa*. Green specimens can at once be recognised in the field, but cream-coloured
examples require closer inspection. This species characteristically
coils up and adopts a grub-like posture when disturbed. Clitellum,
segments 28, or 29–37, tubercula pubertatis, small round elevated
papillae on segments 31, 33 and 35 (fig. 30). Common and widely
distributed in a variety of terrestrial and marshy habitats.

Allolobophora caliginosa (Sav.). Length: 40–70 mm.; diameter
in region of clitellum: 4 mm.; segments: 120–150. Colour pale
pink anteriorly, grey posteriorly. Somewhat similar to specimens
of *A. chlorotica* that lack the characteristic green colour, but the
clitellum is present on segments ½28, 29–34, tubercula pubertatis
on segments 31 and 33, extending over 32 but separated by a
transverse furrow (fig. 29).

One of the most common species known, found in all kinds of
habitats but particularly frequent in cultivated soil, gardens and
also on river banks. It is often the first species to come to the
surface when the soil is vibrated.

Genus *Eisenia*

Prostomium not tanylobous, setae closely paired.

Eisenia rosea (Sav.). Length: 25–85 mm.; diameter: 3–4 mm.;
segments: 120–150. This species can be recognised in the field
by the fact that the first few segments are pink whilst the remainder of the body is flesh-coloured and the clitellum is bright
orange. This lies on segments 24, 25 or 26–32 and 33. Some of
the posterior clitellar segments are somewhat flattened and
broader than the anterior ones. Tubercula pubertatis mostly on
segments 29–31 (fig. 31).

Widely distributed and common everywhere including fields,
gardens, pastures, forests and marshy places.

Eisenia foetida (Sav.). Length: 32–130 mm.; diameter: 3–4

mm.; segments: 80–110. The common Brandling worm can at once be recognised by its transverse stripes or bands of pigment whose red, purple or brown colour alternates with pigmentless yellow intersegmental areas. Clitellum on segments 24, 25 or 26–32, tubercula pubertatis on 28–30.

Common in manure and compost heaps and soil rich in organic matter.

Genus *Dendrobaena*

Small red worms with epilobous prostomium, setae widely paired and tubercula pubertatis present as a band.

Dendrobaena subrubicunda (Eisen.). Length: 27–90 mm.; diameter: 2–4 mm.; segments: 60–110. A small worm with widely paired chaetae, *D. subrubicunda* is easy to recognise as it is flattened dorso-ventrally, reddish in colour with a prominent lighter clitellum on segments 25 or 26–31 and 32. The tubercula pubertatis are oval and occur on segments 28–30.

A widely distributed and common species, sometimes called the Cockspur, occurring in moist places rich in decaying organic matter such as compost and manure heaps.

Genus *Octolasium*

Large blue-grey worms with epilobous prostomium and setae more or less closely paired. Tubercula pubertatis are present as a band. Of the two British species only *O. cyaneum* is sufficiently common to merit description.

Octolasium cyaneum (Sav.). Length: 65–180 mm.; diameter: 7–8 mm.; segments: 104–150. A large pale blue, white or grey worm with the last four or five segments yellow. A pink or orange clitellum lies on segments 29–34. Tubercula pubertatis on segments 30–33 (fig. 32).

A local species usually found under stones or moss in moist habitats.

Genus *Bimastus*

In the common species of this genus the prostomium is epilobous, but it may be tanylobous, as in the rare *B. eiseni* referred to above (p. 42).

Bimastus tenuis (Eisen.). Length: 20–85 mm.; diameter: 3 mm.; segments: 90–120. A small flesh-coloured worm, brown-red dorsally with a bluish tint. Body cylindrical, setae widely paired, clitellum variable, lying between segments 25 and 33; tubercula pubertatis varying between segments 28 and 31, but often indistinct and sometimes absent. Precise identification is seldom possible from external features alone.

Widely distributed under the bark of old trees, moss and in forests under leaf mould and rotten wood, generally in moist localities.

REFERENCES

CERNOSVITOV, L., and EVANS, A. C. (1947). *Synopses of the British fauna No. 6 – Lumbricidae (Annelida)*. London: Linn. Soc.

ROOTS, B. I. (1956). 'Famous animals – 7. The earthworm.' *New Biology* **21**, 102–117.

STEPHENSON, J. (1930). *The Oligochaeta*. Oxford: Clarendon Press.

Chapter Four

WOODLICE

ISOPODA

Woodlice or 'slaters' are among the few crustaceans that are truly terrestrial. They are a particularly interesting group because several common species exhibit different degrees of adaptation to life on land. But none of them can survive in dry air for very long, because they lose water rather quickly by evaporation through their integuments and respiratory organs. Consequently, all species spend most of their lives under stones, bark, fallen logs, leaves and in other damp, dark places and vary only in the length of time during which they are able to wander in the open. The species that lose water the fastest are the most markedly nocturnal in habit and *vice versa*. The physiological adaptations of woodlice to life on land have been discussed in detail by Edney (1954b) and Cloudsley-Thompson (1958) to whom the reader is referred for further information on this aspect of their biology.

Woodlice are included in the sub-order Oniscoidea of the crustacean order Isopoda. They are oval in form and their bodies are arched. The head bears a pair of eyes which, unlike those of lobsters and crabs, are not stalked. There are two large antennae consisting of a *peduncle* and *flagellum* (fig. 34) and a pair of smaller *antennules* in front of them. The head often bears a pair of lateral lobes. The thorax, or *perion*, consists of seven segments which are often broader than the six succeeding ones which form the *abdomen*. Each of the thoracic segments carries a pair of walking limbs. Pairs of *ventral plates* on each of the segments two to five

48

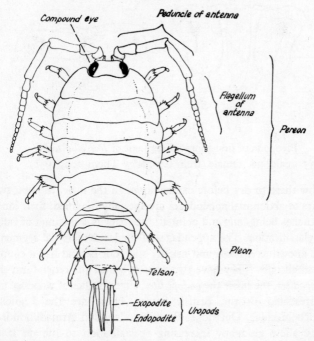

Compound eye

Peduncle of antenna

Flagellum of antenna

Pereon

Pleon

Telson

Exopodite

Endopodite

Uropods

34. *Ligia oceanica*, semi-diagrammatic to show terminology.
(After Edney, 1953)

in mature females together form a *brood pouch* in which the eggs
and newly hatched young are carried.

The appendages of the abdomen or *pleon*, with the exception of
the last pair, are known as *pleopods*. Their inner branches or *rami*
form a surface, while the outer parts act as a protecting cover.
In certain species the pleopods contain breathing tubes or
pseudotracheae, which can be observed under the microscope
(figs. 35 & 36). The pseudotracheae appear white in living woodlice, but are difficult to see in preserved specimens. It is best to

D

49

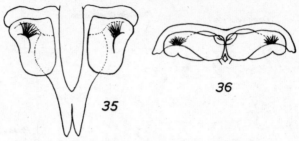

Pleopods of first thoracic segment of *Porcellio scaber*
35. male; 36. female (from Cloudsley-Thompson, 1958)

allow these to dry before examination. In the male, the first two pairs of abdominal appendages are specially modified, their inner branches being long and pointed: the shape is sometimes of value in classification. The appendages of the last abdominal segments are known as *uropods* and usually stick out behind like a couple of small tails. They have two rami of which the outer form the *exopodites*, the inner the *endopodites*. Five families of woodlice are represented in the British fauna. These are the Ligiidae, Trichoniscidae, Oniscidae, Porcellionidae, and Armadillidiidae; they show gradually increasing specialisation to life on land. Thirty-eight British species have been described, of which only the more common and widespread are referred to below. These, however, include the forms most frequently found and those which are of economic importance as pests in gardens. For further information the serious student is referred to Edney's (1953) monograph and his *Synopsis of the British Fauna* published a year later. Webb & Sillem (1906) give some excellent illustrations although their book is quite out of date in other respects.

Family *Ligiidae*

There are two British species in this family one of which, *Ligia oceanica*, the well-known sea-slater, is very common; the other,

Ligidium hypnorum, somewhat rare. The body is regularly oblong oval, fully convex above. Head without lobes, eyes large and legs increasing in length posteriorly.

Ligia oceanica (L.). (figs. 37 & 47) This is the largest of the British woodlice, up to 30 mm. long, rather more than twice as long as broad. The upper surface of the body is covered with small tubercles. The head is without lobes, rather more than twice as wide as long. This species is easily recognisable and unlikely to be confused with any other.

Colour, greenish-grey with black eyes. These animals show well-marked colour change due to the expansion or contraction of colour pigment cells, so that they tend to become pale when placed on a white background and dark on a black background. In addition they become pale at night and darker by day.

The legs are long and the animal can run surprisingly fast. The antenna lacks conspicuous spines, the flagellum consisting of 11 to 15 segments. The uropods are long and wholly visible from above, their rami being more than ten times as long as wide at the base.

This species is restricted to the seashore all round the British Isles. It is to be found in crevices of rock and under rotting seaweed above high-tide mark, but seldom far from the splash zone.

Ligidium hypnorum (Cuv.) (fig. 48). Up to 11 mm. long, rather more than twice as long as wide. Somewhat resembling a small *Ligia oceanica* in general appearance. Head without lobes, nearly twice as wide as long. Upper surface of body smooth.

Colour, variable, often a pale ochre with dark, irregular patches becoming continuous near each side of the thorax.

Antennae with a small number of distinct spines, the terminal segment of the peduncle five times as long as wide at the base. Legs again rather long compared with those of other species. Outer ramus of uropods four times as long as the inner and five times as long as wide at the base.

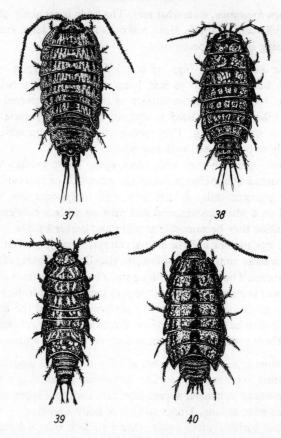

37. *Ligia oceanica*; 38. *Ligidium hypnorum*; 39. *Trichoniscus pusillus*; 40. *Philoscia muscorum*

(After Webb & Sillem, 1906)

Restricted to damp environments as far north as Lancashire. Not recorded from Scotland or Ireland.

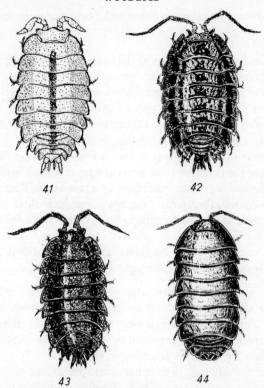

41. *Platyarthrus hoffmannseggi*; 42. *Oniscus asellus*;
43. *Porcellio scaber*; 44. *Armadillidium vulgare*
(After Webb & Sillem, 1906)

Family *Trichoniscidae*

Small, elongated animals having a head with lateral lobes, spiney antennae and eyes reduced or absent. Of 13 British species, only *Trichoniscus pusillus* is really common, but since *Androniscus dentiger* has a striking delicate rose-pink colour in life and seldom

53

fails to arouse interest when discovered, both species are described below.

Trichoniscus pusillus (Brandt) (fig. 49). Not more than 4 mm. in length and a little more than twice as long as wide. Head nearly twice as wide as long; the lateral lobes well developed, each bearing about four spines. The upper surface of the body is steeply arched with parallel sides, and thinly covered with short hairs.

Colour, a mottled reddish-brown; sometimes purple.

Antennae of medium length with a few long spines, the last segment of the peduncle three times as long as wide. Flagellum of four indistinct segments terminated by a fine brush. Rami of the uropods conical, their outer branches (exopodites) three times as long as wide at the base: endopodites shorter and only half as wide at the base.

Very common locally in moist places under fallen leaves, especially in beech woods throughout the British Isles.

Androniscus dentiger (Verh.) (fig. 50). Up to 5·5 mm. in length, twice or slightly more times as long as wide. Dorsal surface covered with tubercles, lateral lobes long, with spiny margins.

This species is easily recognised by its bright pink colour which fades when the animal is preserved in alcohol.

Antennae fairly long with rather short spines. Last peduncular segment four times as long as wide. Rami of uropods conical, the exopodites four times as long as wide at the base, endopodites shorter and narrower.

Widespread but not common. Sometimes found in rubble and refuse heaps.

Family *Oniscidae*

Small to large animals with compound eyes (absent in *Platyarthrus*). Pleopods without pseudotracheae. Flagellar segments distinct, never exceeding three in number. Legs often long and spiny: rami of the uropods visible from above. There are five British species.

Philoscia muscorum (Scop.) (figs. 40 & 51). Up to 10 mm. in length, but only twice as long as wide. Oval in outline, but the base of the pleon is distinctly narrower than the pereion. Integument smooth and shiny.

Colour, various shades of brown or grey with attractive darker mottled marking, head often black.

Antennae long and relatively hairless. Exopodites of the uropods twice as wide at the base as the endopodites and four times as long as wide. The legs are comparatively long and the animal runs surprisingly quickly when disturbed.

Widespread in moist situations such as rubbish heaps, the carpet of dead leaves in woods and so on.

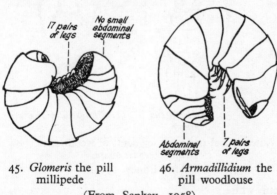

45. *Glomeris* the pill millipede

46. *Armadillidium* the pill woodlouse

(From Sankey, 1958)

Platyarthrus hoffmannseggi (Brandt) (figs. 41 & 52). Up to 3·6 mm. long, oval in outline and less than twice as long as wide. Covered with minute scale-like spines. Head with strong lateral lobes.

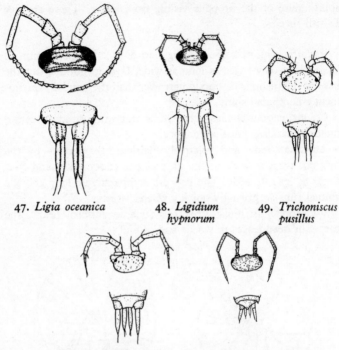

47. *Ligia oceanica*　　48. *Ligidium*　　49. *Trichoniscus*
　　　　　　　　　　　　　hypnorum　　　　*pusillus*

50. *Androniscus*　　51. *Philoscia muscorum*
　　dentiger

Anterior and posterior segments of woodlice to show
characteristic shape
(After Edney, 1953)

Colour, white.

Eyes absent, antennae and exopodites of uropods short and
stout: endopodites hidden by the pointed telson.

Widespread in the nests of ants.

Oniscus asellus (L.) (figs. 42 & 53). One of the largest and commonest woodlice, up to 15 mm. long and twice as long as wide.

56

52. *Platyarthrus hoffmannseggi*   53. *Oniscus asellus*   54. *Porcellio scaber*

55. *Porcellio spinicornis*   56. *Armadillidium vulgare*

Anterior and posterior segments of woodlice to show characteristic shape. (After Edney, 1953)

Readily distinguished from *Porcellio scaber* (p. 58) by the absence of tubercles and its slightly shiny integument.

Colour, usually slaty grey with irregular lighter markings.

Antennae with very fine hairs. Last segment of peduncle the longest, seven times as long as wide. Flagellum shorter than this and composed of three segments. Exopodites of uropods two and a half times as long as wide, endopodites much narrower.

Ubiquitous. Aggregates in large numbers beneath stones, bark, fallen trees and similar sheltered places.

Family *Porcellionidae*

Large animals with compound eyes and pseudotracheae. Flagellum with two distinct segments. Rami of uropods usually visible from above. Ten British species have been recorded.

Porcellio scaber (Latr.) (figs. 43 & 54). Up to 17 mm. in length and nearly twice as long as wide. Easily recognised and distinguishable from *Oniscus asellus* by the tubercles with which the dorsal surface is covered, giving the animal a mat appearance. Frontal lobe of head triangular with strong lateral lobes.

Colour, very variable; usually a dark slaty grey, sometimes with irregular, light markings.

Antennae with last peduncular segment six times as long as wide and one-fourth or less as long again as the flagellum. First two pairs of pleopods with pseudotracheae. Exopodites of uropods about two and a half times as long as wide. Endopodites shorter, tubular in shape.

This, with *Oniscus asellus*, is the commonest British woodlouse, widely distributed under bark, fallen leaves and so on. Sometimes found quite high up trees.

Porcellio spinicornis (Say) (fig. 55). Length up to 12 mm., about twice as long as wide. Appearance similar to that of *P. scaber* from which it can be distinguished by the fact that the anterior margin of the frontal lobe is continuously rounded over the whole of its length. (In *P. scaber* the frontal lobe is triangular.)

Colour, dark brown with yellowish markings. Head often black.

Appendages, similar to *P. scaber*, but the endopodites of the uropods are larger, nearly three-quarters as long as the exopodites.

Widely distributed especially on heathland, sand-dunes and similar places.

Family *Armadillidiidae*

Body strongly convex, capable of rolling into a ball. Legs comparatively short. First two pairs of pleopods with pseudotracheae. There are eight British species.

Armadillidium vulgare (Latr.) (figs. 44 & 56). This is the common 'pill-woodlouse' and should not be confused with the 'pill-millipede', *Glomeris marginata*. (*Armadillidium* has seven pairs of legs and a small posterior abdominal segment; *Glomeris* has 17 pairs of legs, normal abdominal segments, a large and characteristic tergite behind the head and a more glossy appearance.) Up to 18 mm. in length and slightly more than twice as long as wide.

Colour varied, from black to pale yellow. Usually grey.

Last peduncular segment of the antenna six times as long as wide and about one-fifth as long again as the flagellum. Uropods not visible from above.

Widely distributed, especially calcareous soils. More frequently wandering in the open during the day-time than other species of woodlouse.

REFERENCES

CLOUDSLEY-THOMPSON, J. L. (1958) *Spiders, scorpions, centipedes and mites.* London: Pergamon.

EDNEY, E. B. (1953) *The woodlice of Great Britain and Ireland. A concise systematic monograph.* Proc. Linn. Soc. Lond. **164,** 49–98.

EDNEY, E. B. (1954a) *Synopses of the British fauna No.* 9 – *British woodlice.* London: Linn. Soc.

EDNEY, E. B. (1954b) 'Woodlice and the land habitat'. *Biol. Rev.* **89,** 385–542.

WEBB, W. M., and SILLEM, C. (1906) *The British woodlice.* London, Duckworth.

Chapter Five

MILLIPEDES

DIPLOPODA

The Class Diplopoda includes many-legged animals, commonly called millipedes, in which most of the segments of the body are provided with two pairs of limbs. The anterior portions of these diplo-segments are referred to as *prozonites*, the wider posterior regions as *metazonites*. In the families Polydesmidae, Strongylosomidae and Craspedosomidae, the latter are extended to form lateral or dorso-lateral keels.

Millipedes have a distinct head bearing a pair of short eight-segmented *antennae*, a pair of *mandibles*, *maxillae* fused to form a broad plate or *gnathochilarium* and often eyes. *Spiracles* leading into tubular *tracheae* open above the *coxae* of the legs and the dorsal plates of the segments are greatly developed as compared with the ventral. The trunk is terminated by a variable number of legless diplo-segments, the last of which is the *telson*, which, dorsally, may form a 'tail' whose shape may be a diagnostic character, and there is a pair of *anal valves*. The reproductive organs have their apertures on the ventral side of the fore part of the body near the head, whereas in centipedes these open on the last abdominal segment as they do in insects. In the males usually one or two pairs of legs are modified for mating purposes and their structure is a diagnostic character in many species. Blower (1958) gives a clear account of the general body organisation of these animals.

Millipedes are essentially animals of the soil, some, including the Polydesmidae and Craspedosomidae, inhabiting woodland litter whilst others actually penetrate into the earth. The latter are especially susceptible to desiccation, under the influence of which they tend to move deeper into the ground. At the same time they become water-logged very easily, so their environment must be neither too wet nor too dry. Consequently they are ideally placed in a litter layer which is proof against both flood and drought. Although they are vegetarians, feeding on a wide range of plant substances, millipedes have also been recorded as eating dead worms, molluscs, insects and other animals.

The presence of *repugnatorial stink glands* along the side of the body renders millipedes distasteful to most enemies. Although they are eaten by a wide range of predatory animals, only toads and birds feed on them to an appreciable degree.

Several species enclose their eggs in little nests, constructed of earth and excrement, which protect them from attack by fungi. Not infrequently, the female remains with them during the period of incubation. Growth is accompanied by moulting, as in other arthropods, after which it is customary for the animals to eat their cast integument, thus restoring lost supplies of calcium. For further details of natural history and behaviour, the reader is referred to the book by Cloudsley-Thompson (1958).

The British millipede fauna comprises some 44 species and includes representatives of each of the six major groups of Diplopoda. Many of these, however, are rare and will probably not be encountered unless specially sought for. The 13 most common species are described below: for the identification of others, the reader is referred to Blower's (1958) excellent synopsis of the British millipedes, upon which this chapter is largely based, and to the monograph by Schubart (1934).

Sub-class PSELAPHOGNATHA
Family *Polyxenidae*
Polyxenus lagurus (L.) (fig. 57). The sub-class Pselaphognatha

contains but one European species. This differs from all other millipedes in having a cuticle that is not hardened with calcium salts but covered with variously serrated hollow spines. These are arranged in two transverse rows united by lateral tufts on the head and body segments. Terminally, two long brushes are borne on the telson. This tiny animal is a light amber colour with dark brown

57. *Polyxenus lagurus*

spines. It is unlikely to be confused with any other animal but may not at first be recognised as a millipede either. *P. lagurus* occurs under stones, bark and in leaf litter both inland and on the shore in coastal regions. A favourite habitat is beneath lichen on walls and trees.

Length: 2-3 mm.; breadth: 0·5-1 mm.

Sub-class CHILOGNATHA

This sub-class includes the 'true' Diplopoda with a hard cuticle impregnated with calcium salts.

Family *Glomeridae*

Pill-millipedes, which comprise this family, should not be confused with woodlice. There are 12 apparent tergites, 17 pairs of legs in the female and 19 pairs in the male, of which the last three are modified for reproductive purposes.

Glomeris marginata (Vill.) (fig. 58). The common pill-millipede can be distinguished from the woodlouse, *Armadillidium*

58. *Glomeris marginata*

vulgare (p. 59), by its more shiny cuticle, the large shield-like tergite behind the head, the absence of small abdominal segments,
its short seven-segmented antennae and the greater number of
legs. Once it has curled up, *G. marginata* shows a much greater
reluctance to uncurl. The majority of specimens are glossy black
in colour but yellow, brown and red variations occur. *G. marginata*
is common amongst fallen leaves and where the soil is calcareous
it is especially plentiful, extending its range to fields and hedges.

Length: ♂ 7–15 mm., ♀ 8–20 mm.
Breadth: ♂ 3·5–6 mm., ♀ 4–8 mm.

Family *Polydesmidae*

Flat-backed millipedes with dorso-lateral keels. The back is elab-
orately sculptured. There are no eyes.

Brachydesmus superus (Latzel) (fig. 59). The body comprises
19 segments, light brown or cream in colour.

Commonly associated with farmland, this species is the only
member of the family habitually found in the soil. It is common
in caves.

Length: 8–10 mm.; breadth: 0·8–1 mm.

Polydesmus angustus (Latzel). The genus *Polydesmus* can be
distinguished from *Brachydesmus* by the presence of 20 segments
in the adult. *P. angustus* is the largest and most common British

species. Its colour varies through various shades of brown and it can be found in a variety of habitats, under stones, beneath bark, logs and fallen leaves. Sometimes frequent in gardens and around farms.

Length: 16–28·5 mm.; breadth: 2·8–5 mm.

Family *Strongylosomidae*

Members of this family are superficially similar to the Polydesmidae but can be distinguished by the fact that the body is narrower, the tergites arched and not flat, the keels less well developed and tubercles absent.

Oxidus gracilis (C. L. Koch) (fig. 60). A tropical species that has been distributed all over the world by human agency. In temperate regions it is a common inhabitant of greenhouses. Body segments 20, colour a deep reddish-brown, keels well developed, lateral rather than dorsal in position. Eyes absent.

Length: ♂ 16–21 mm., ♀ 17–23 mm.
Breadth: ♂ 2–2·3 mm., ♀ 2–2·5 mm.

Family *Craspedosomidae*

Moderate sized, flat-backed millipedes with well-defined simple eyes or ocelli in a triangular group. Body segments 30.

Polymicrodon polydesmoides (Leach). Fawn to dark brown in colour with well-developed dorso-lateral keels giving the appearance of a Polydesmid millipede, from which it can be distinguished by the number of segments and the presence of eyes. A very common species of woodland litter especially where the soil is calcareous; occurring also in open country, but less frequently in farmland.

Length: 17–21 mm.; breadth: 2–2·5 mm.

Family *Blaniulidae*

Slender cylindrical millipedes seldom exceeding 1 mm. in

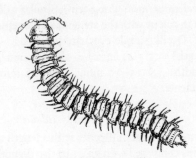

59. *Brachydesmus superus*   60. *Oxidus gracilis*

61. *Blaniulus guttulatus*

62. *Tachypodoiulus niger*
Typical millipedes (From Cloudsley-Thompson, 1958)

diameter and whitish, creamy or light brown in colour, often with a row of dark spots along the sides of the body.

Blaniulus guttulatus (Bosc) (fig. 61). The 'spotted snake-millipede', a well-known agricultural pest, *B. guttulatus* can be recognised by the absence of eyes and the fact that the contents of the repugnatorial glands are bright red in life and appear as a row of spots along the sides of the body.

Length: ♂ 7·5–14 mm., ♀ 9–18 mm.
Breadth: ♂ 0·4–0·6 mm., ♀ 0·45–0·7 mm.
Segments: ♂ 37–50,   ♀ 41–60.

Proteroiulus fuscus (Am Stein). Similar to *B. guttulatus*, but dark brown in colour with the contents of the repugnatorial glands even darker. Ocelli (simple eyes) are present.

Length: ♂ 7–11 mm., ♀ 7–15 mm.
Breadth: ♂ 0·5–0·7 mm., ♀ 0·5–0·8 mm.
Segments: ♂ 31–37, ♀ 31–45.

Family *Iulidae*

Stouter cylindrical millipedes with a length to breadth ratio about 10 : 1 (as compared with 20 : 1 in the Blaniulidae). Ocelli present, telson usually produced into a dorso-median 'tail'. Often of darker coloration than Blaniulidae. Iulid millipedes frequently exhibit the phenomenon of periodomorphosis: adult males may regress, alternating with a series of intercalary forms which lack the highly differentiated gonopods of the mature animal.

In the following paragraphs are given descriptions of some of the commonest and *easily recognisable* species. Two common black millipedes which may be confused with *Tachypodoiulus niger* are *Iulus scandinavius* (Latzel) and *Ophyiulus pilosus* (Newport). However, they both have a much longer hyaline apex to the telson which does *not* curve upwards: in addition, they are more hairy than *T. niger*. As they are rather difficult to distinguish from one another, the student is referred to the monograph by Blower (1958) for further information.

Tachypodoiulus niger (Leach) (figs. 62 & 63). The common black millipede, often erroneously confused with *Iulus terrestris*, a continental species that does not occur in the British Isles. Immature specimens are brown, the adults and later immature stadia black with white legs. The telson is produced into a pointed caudal projection with a clear hyaline apex which is curved upwards dorsally. Hairs are scattered along its whole length. The prozonites of each diplo-segment show distinct transverse chas-

66

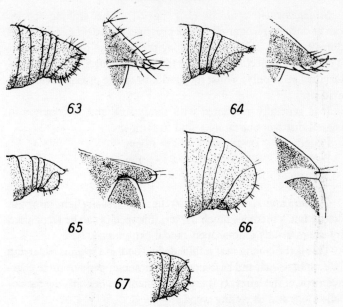

The telson in various species of Iulidae
63. *Tachypodoiulus niger*; 64. *Schizophyllum sabulosum*;
65. *Cylindroiulus punctatus*; 66. *Cylindroiulus londinensis*;
67. *Cylindroiulus latestriatus*. (After Blower, 1958)

ings. Very young specimens have a coloration similar to that of *Schizophyllum sabulosum*.

This active species is widely distributed throughout the British Isles, especially in chalk and limestone districts where it is common under bark, fallen logs, rocks and stones. Specimens usually emerge from their retreats at night to feed upon vegetable matter, encrusting algae, fallen fruit and so on.

Length: ♂ 19–45 mm., ♀ 20–49 mm.
Breadth: ♂ 1·8–2·5 mm., ♀ 2–3·1 mm.
Segments: ♂ 41–56, ♀ 44–56.

Schizophyllum sabulosum (L.) (fig. 64). This striking species can at once be recognised by the presence of two orange-coloured dorso-median stripes running along the length of the black body.[1] The caudal projection is similar to that of *T. niger*, but with sub-terminal setae only; whilst the markings on the prozonites are less evident.

It is generally associated with sandy soils and is common in coastal districts but rarely found in farmland.

Length: ♂ 15–28 mm.,   ♀ 21–47 mm.
Breadth: ♂ 1·6–2·5 mm., ♀ 2·1–4 mm.
Segments: ♂ 45–54,   ♀ 46–55.

Cylindroiulus punctatus (Leach) (fig. 65). Usually light brown in colour but sometimes much darker, this species can be recognised by the markedly club-shaped caudal extremity.

This is the commonest millipede in woodland regions occurring in both base-rich and base-poor soils although perhaps more characteristic of the latter. It is especially common beneath the bark of fallen logs and in rotting wood.

Length: ♂ 13–20 mm.,   ♀ 15·28 mm.
Breadth: ♂ 1·2–1·4 mm., ♀ 1·4–2·1 mm.
Segments: ♂ 46–53,   ♀ 47–58.

Cylindroiulus londinensis (Leach) (fig. 66). A large black or dark grey millipede usually with the telson not produced, but occasionally very large specimens may possess a slightly produced telson. Immature specimens may be paler than the adults which have a characteristic metallic appearance and can be distinguished from other black or dark brown Iulids by the fact that their bodies are of roughly the same diameter from head to tail.

This is a true soil species maintaining large populations in

---

[1] The small *Brachyiulus pusillus* (Leach) has similar markings but no pointed tail.

arable and grassland as well as in woods, but nearly always in calcareous districts.

Length: 18–50 mm.; breadth 1·6–4 mm.

Segments: ♂ 38–48, ♀ 39–53.

Cylindroiulus latestriatus (Curtis) (fig. 67). Although usually dark brown in colour, light brown specimens are sometimes found. The telson is not produced and has a rounded posterior extremity. There are three pairs of setae on the anal valves.

This species is common in coastal regions, in sand dunes and on cliffs, as well as inland where the soil is sandy.

Length: ♂ 9–14 mm.,   ♀ 13–19 mm.

Breadth: ♂ 0·7–1 mm.,   ♀ 1·1–1·4 mm.

Segments: ♂ 34–44,   ♀ 41–50.

REFERENCES

BLOWER, J. G. (1958) *Synopses of the British fauna No. 11 – British millipedes (Diplopoda)*. London: Linn. Soc.

CLOUDSLEY-THOMPSON, J. L. (1958) *Spiders, scorpions, centipedes and mites*. London: Pergamon.

SCHUBART, O. (1934) Tausendfüssler oder Myriapoda, I. Diplopoda *Tierw. Deuts.*, **28**, 1–318.

Chapter Six

CENTIPEDES

CHILOPODA

Centipedes (class Chilopoda) are shy and elusive in their habits, so that they tend to escape anything more than cursory notice. Whilst the British species are small and innocuous, their tropical relatives reach a considerable size and can inflict painful wounds. Centipedes are active predators, feeding on spiders, insects and their larvae, woodlice, collembolans, worms and other small creatures. Certain of the Geophilomorpha, however, such as *Haplophilus subterraneus*, will, on occasion, feed upon plant tissues and may even be positively injurious to crops.

The British species are classified into three orders. The first, Geophilomorpha ('earth-lovers') (fig. 68) comprises a number of attenuated species which usually occur deep in the soil. Their form is adapted for burrowing. The remaining orders, Scolopendromorpha (fig. 69) and Lithobiomorpha (fig. 70) ('stone-dwellers'), comprise various speedy forms with longer legs and a reduced number of body segments. They live in damp, dark and obscure places under stones, fallen leaves, logs, under bark and in crevices of the soil from which they issue forth at night in search of prey. For, like woodlice and millipedes, etc., centipedes lack a water-proofing wax-layer.

An indirect method of fertilisation occurs in centipedes. The male deposits a *spermatophore* (a bag containing spermatozoa) which is later taken up by the female. In the Lithobiomorpha the eggs are laid individually in the soil after being covered with earth

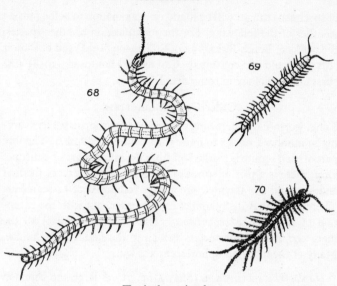

Typical centipedes
68. *Necrophlaeophagus longicornis* (family Geophilidae);
69. *Cryptops hortensis* (family Cryptopsidae); 70. *Lithobius forficatus* (family Lithobiidae). (From Cloudsley-Thompson, 1958)

by the female, but in the Geophilomorpha and Scolopendro-morpha the young are usually guarded by their mother until they are able to look after themselves. If separated from their parent the eggs usually become infected with fungus and die within a few days.

The young of Lithobiomorpha centipedes hatch with seven pairs of legs: additional leg-bearing segments are added during development. In the remaining orders the young emerge from the egg-shell with the full number of legs. About 40 British species have been discovered, but many of these are rare and the majority of specimens caught will be found on examination to belong to one or other of the following. For the identification of other species, the works of Brade-Birks (1929), Brölemann (1932) and of Blower (1955) should be consulted. Cloudsley-Thompson (1958) discusses their biology in some detail.

Order **Geophilomorpha**

Long, worm-like, burrowing centipedes with the pairs of legs varying in number from 37 to more than twice this number. The fore part of each somite is marked off from the hinder part by a distinct joint, there is a pair of spiracles on each segment except the first and last, and the antennae are always composed of 14 segments. There are four British families in this order, but with the exception of *Haplophilus subterraneus* (family Himantariidae) all the more common of our species belong to the family Geophilidae. Many of them are phosphorescent at night.

Haplophilus subterraneus (Shaw) (fig. 71). A large and common species of gardens and woodlands, easily recognised by the length and extensibility of the body as well as by the number of segments. It is usually a pale yellow colour and the terminal limbs are clawless. A central pore field can be distinguished on the anterior sternites: the antennae are short and stumpy.

Length: up to 75 mm.; legs ♂ 69–87, ♀ 73–89.

Geophilus carpophagus (Leach) (fig. 72). This is undoubtedly the commonest species of non-cultivated districts and open country. Its comparatively robust body, somewhat tapering at the extremities, is usually of a more sombre colour than that of other Geophilids. The ventral plates of the anterior body segments have a typical 'carpophagus' articulation (fig. 72b). The posterior border of each anterior sternite has a small but definite projection which fits into a correspondingly small pit on the anterior border of the succeeding sternite. The anterior excavations of the ventral plates are only one-third the width of the plates themselves. The antennal segments are somewhat bead-like in shape.

Length: up to 70 mm.; legs ♂ 47–57, ♀ 49–59.

Geophilus insculptus (Attems) (fig. 73). This species is structurally similar to *G. carpophagus* although it looks different, being light yellow in colour with the gut contents showing through the cuticle. When preserved it can be distinguished by the fact that the socket of the anterior ventral plates is large, being nearly as wide as the plates themselves.

Length: up to 30 mm.; legs ♂ 43–47, ♀ 47–63.

Necrophlaeophagus longicornis (Leach) (fig. 74). A very common species easily recognised by the long antennal segments, three times as long as broad, and their clothing of long hairs. The carpophagus structure is entirely absent.

Length: up to 44 mm.; legs ♂ 41–53, ♀ 43–57

Brachygeophilus truncorum (Berg. & Mein.) (fig. 75). One of the smallest British species, recognised by the fact that each of the anterior sternites is furnished with three distinct, broad, longitudinal grooves which practically occupy the whole plate. There are usually 39 pairs of legs.

Length: up to 18 mm.; legs ♂ 37–39, ♀ 37–41.

Scolioplanes acuminatus (Leach) (= *S. crassipes*) (fig. 76). An active, rich reddish-brown species whose identification may be confirmed by the presence of a *large* internal tooth near the base of the poison claw.

Length: up to 56 mm.; legs ♂ 39–57, ♀ 41–59.

Scolioplanes maritimus (Leach) (fig. 77). The second British species of the genus *Scolioplanes* is widely distributed along our shores under rocks and stones covered at high tide. It has been recorded emerging at night and feeding on barnacles attached to

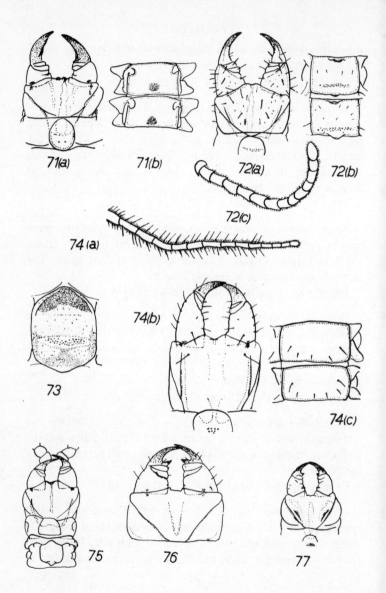

71(a)   71(b)   72(a)   72(b)

72(c)

74(a)

74(b)

73   74(c)

75   76   77

rocks. The internal tooth of the poison claw is much weaker than in the preceding species.

Length: up to 31 mm.; legs ♂ & ♀ 47–53.

Order **Scolopendromorpha**

The order Scolopendromorpha contains two families, the Scolopendridae and the Cryptopsidae, of which the former includes most of the large tropical and sub-tropical centipedes having 21 pairs of legs. Only the Cryptopsidae is represented in the British fauna by a number of species of which one is not uncommon.

Cryptops hortensis (Leach) (fig. 69). This species can at once be recognised by the presence of 22 body segments, 21 pairs of legs, and its orange colour. It reaches a length of 25 mm. and has antennae composed of 17 segments.

Order **Lithobiomorpha**

Lithobiomorph centipedes differ from the Scolopendromorpha in having the body composed of 15 leg-bearing somites behind the one bearing the poison claws, of which only six or seven possess spiracles, the terga of those without spiracles being reduced in size. The majority of the British species can be referred to the family Lithobiidae.

Diagnostic characters of Geophilomorph centipedes

71. *Haplophilus subterraneus* (a) Poison claws and first leg-bearing sternite. (b) Sternites of segments 42 and 43 showing central pore field; 72. *Geophilus carpophagus* (a) Poison claws and first leg-bearing sternite, (b) Sternites of segments 8 and 9, showing carpophagus structure, (c) Antenna; 73. *Geophilus insculptatus*. Sternite of 15th segment; 74. *Necrophlaeophagus longicornis* (a) Antenna, (b) Poison claws, (c) Sternites of segments 8 and 9; 75. *Brachygeophilus truncorum*. Poison claw and first leg-bearing segments; 76. *Scolioplanes acuminatus*. Poison claws; 77. *Scolioplanes maritimus*. Poison claws. (After Brölemann, 1932 and original)

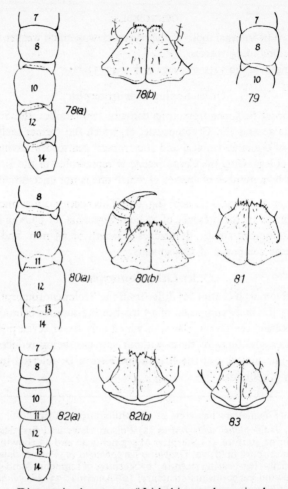

Diagnostic characters of Lithobiomorph centipedes

78. *Lithobius forficatus* (a) Tergites 7–14, (b) Coxosternites of maxillipedes; 79. *Lithobius variegatus*. Tergites 7–10; 80. *Lithobius melanops* (a) Tergites 8–14, (b) Coxosternites of maxillipedes; 81. *Lithobius calcaratus*. Coxosternites of maxillipedes; 82. *Lithobius crassipes* (a) Tergites 7–14, (b) Coxosternites of maxillipedes; 83. *Lithobius duboscqui*. Coxosternites of maxillipedes. (After Brolemann, 1932, and original)

Lithobius forficatus (L.) (figs. 70 & 78). This large and handsome species is frequently associated with human dwellings and gardens. It can be distinguished from *L. variegatus*, the other common large British species, by its dark brown colour and the fact that the 7th tergite is not produced posteriorly although the 9th is. Length varies from 18 to 32 mm. and there are usually about 6 small teeth on the front edge of the basal segment of each maxillipede coxosternite.

Lithobius variegatus (Leach) (fig. 79). This attractive centipede can at once be recognised in the field by its size, its tawny coloration and variegated legs.

In many districts it replaces *L. forficatus*, particularly at high altitudes, but it appears to be confined to the British Isles. The 7th, 9th, 11th and 13th tergites have definite posterior prolongations although those of the 7th are less pronounced than the others, and again there are usually about 6 small teeth on each maxillipede coxosternite.

Length: 18·5–23 mm.

Lithobius melanops (Newport) (fig. 80). A small, active centipede often found beneath the bark of fallen trees, it is also frequent in maritime situations. It measures 10–17 mm. in length, is yellowish-brown in colour and has 2 teeth on each maxillipede coxosternite. The antennae are composed of 34–46 segments, tergites 9, 11 and 13 have posterior prolongations and there are 11–16 ocelli.

Lithobius calcaratus (C. L. Koch) (fig. 81). This species can be recognised in the field by its deep, almost black colour. It is often to be found under stones and grass or chalk downs and heathland. Measuring 10–15 mm. in length, *L. calcaratus* has 2 teeth on the coxosternite of each maxillipede, antennae composed of 39–56 segments, 7–9 ocelli and tergites not produced posteriorly.

LAND INVERTEBRATES

Lithobius crassipes (L. Koch) (fig. 82). This is perhaps the most typical species occurring among rich leaf litter in woods. It measures 6–10·5 mm. in length, has 2 teeth on the coxosternite of each maxillipede, antennae composed of 20 segments, 8–11 ocelli and tergites not produced posteriorly.

Lithobius duboscqui (Bröl.) (fig. 83). The smallest British member of the genus, measuring only 5–8 mm. in length, *L. duboscqui* can be recognised in the field by the fact that it curls up on being disturbed. It is often to be found in arable land. The colouring is uniformly yellow, there are 2 robust teeth on the coxosternite of each maxillipede, short antennae of 25 segments, 3 ocelli on each side, and the tergites are not produced posteriorly.

REFERENCES

BLOWER, G. (1955) 'Yorkshire centipedes'. *Naturalist* No. 855, 137–46.

BRADE-BIRKS, S. G. (1929) 'Notes on Myriapoda XXXIII. The economic status of Diplopoda and Chilopoda and their allies. Part 1'. *J. S.-E. Agric. Coll. Wye* No. 26, 178–216.

BRÖLEMANN, H. W. (1932) 'Chilopodes'. *Faune de France*, **25**, 1–405.

CLOUDSLEY-THOMPSON, J. L. (1958) *Spiders, scorpions, centipedes and mites*. London: Pergamon.

EASON, E. H. (1964) *Centipedes of the British Isles*. London: Warne.

Chapter Seven

PAUROPODS AND SYMPHYLIDS

PAUROPODA AND SYMPHYLA

When a stone or log is turned over, or leaf litter disturbed, especially in moist situations, a number of tiny, whitish animals are to be seen. Most of them spring about in lively fashion; these are 'spring-tails' or Collembola, a group of animals previously regarded as primitive wingless insects, but now recognised as belonging to a separate class. Collembola are extremely numerous in the soil, but not all species spring. Like insects, they possess six legs and a body divided into head, thorax and abdomen. The antennae are usually four-segmented and the abdomen is divided into six segments. An adhesive *ventral tube* is usually found on the first of these, a minute hook or *hamula* on the third and a forked springing organ on the fourth. We have not included Collembola in this book, because they are dealt with in many entomological works and, at best, constitute a 'specialist' group.

If one's gaze is not too distracted by the antics of the spring-tails, a number of smaller, many-legged animals may also be noticed before they scurry under cover. Of these the very smallest are probably Pauropoda (fig. 84), a class of tiny arthropods measuring only about one-twentieth of an inch in length. They can be recognised by their distinctly branched antennae and the body of twelve segments. There are ten pairs of limbs when adult, of which nine have a locomotory function, the first pair being reduced to mere buds. In addition, the legs are widely spaced, and there are five pairs of long, tactile bristles attached to the sides of the body.

There is, as yet, no satisfactory English publication that will enable the student to identify specimens. In any case, on account of their small size, the Pauropoda are inevitably a 'specialist' group. For further information and bibliography, the reader is

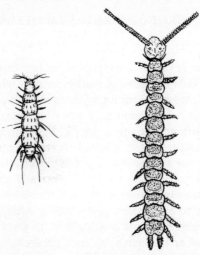

84. *Pauropus*   85. *Scutigerella immaculata*
(From Cloudsley-Thompson, 1958)

advised to consult the relevant chapter in Cloudsley-Thompson (1958).

Another class of common but small inhabitants of the şoil is the Symphyla (fig. 85). Its representatives have long, many-segmented antennae, 15–22 tergites and 11 or 12 pairs of walking legs when adult. The length of the body averages about 4 mm. in British species. Both Pauropoda and Symphyla appear to be primarily of vegetarian habits. Some species of the latter class sometimes reach sufficiently large populations to be of considerable economic importance, since they will attack almost any plant possessing a delicate root system.

Pauropoda and Symphyla can be collected by placing a quantity of the soil in which they live in a container of water. When the water is stirred, these soil animals float to the surface and can be picked up with a fine brush. They should be preserved in 70% alcohol to which a little glycerine may be added. For determination they may be mounted temporarily in lactic acid under a cover slip and gently warmed for about 10 minutes to clear them. Less common species can be indentified from the useful monograph by Edwards (1959), on which the following account has been based. Only adults can be determined with certainty.

Class SYMPHYLA
Family *Scutigerellidae*

The members of this family are usually more than 4 mm. in length and very active. The head is distinctly separated from the neck, dorsal tergites are large, curved and distinct. There are large *styli* at the base of the legs. The *cerci* do not have any stripes at the tip.

Scutigerella immaculata (Newp.) (figs. 85, 86). A cosmopolitan species, frequently a pest of cultivated crops, *S. immaculata* can most easily be found around the roots of growing plants, especially in moist soil. The dorsal tergites or scuta, particularly the anterior ones, are moderately curved inwards posteriorly.

Length: 5·5–7 mm.

S. causeyae (Michelbacher) (fig. 87). This species is more common in forest litter and in soils containing a high proportion of organic matter. The posterior margin of the second scutum is

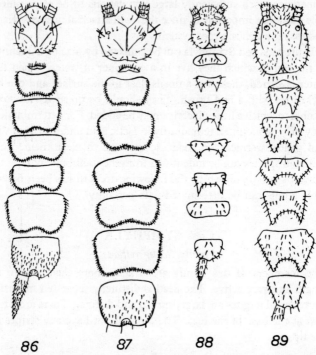

86   87   88   89

Dorsal views of the head, first six and terminal scuta of
Symphyla

86. *Scutigerella immaculata*; 87. *Scutigerella causeyae*;
88. *Symphylellopsis subnuda*; 89. *Symphylella vulgaris*. (After
Edwards, 1959)

almost linear. Chaetae are long and numerous, especially on the
cerci.

Length: 5·1–8·2 mm.

Family *Scolopendrellidae*

Species usually less than 4 mm. in length and rather sluggish.

Head not distinctly separated from the neck, dorsal tergites are small and usually have paired triangular projections on the posterior margins of the scuta. The styli at the base of the legs are very small and the cerci have transverse or longitudinal stripes at the tip.

Symphylella vulgaris (Hansen) (fig. 89). A very slow-moving species probably feeding on decaying matter and bacteria in the soil. Oval head with about 19 antennal segments. Only 17 dorsal scuta including the first, which is represented only by chaetae. Cerci long with small expanded terminal area. Only 11 pairs of legs when adult, the first represented by small protuberances. Length: 2·4–3·5 mm.

Symphylellopsis subnuda (Hansen) (fig. 88). A very small, slow-moving species, with about 16 antennal segments and 22 indistinct scuta, only some of which possess long, narrow, triangular projections. Cerci short with a long conical terminal area. Length: 1·2–2 mm.

REFERENCES

CLOUDSLEY-THOMPSON, J. L. (1958) *Spiders, scorpions, centipedes and mites*. London: Pergamon.

EDWARDS, C. A. (1959) 'A revision of the British Symphyla'. *Proc. Zool. Soc. Lond.* **132,** 403–439.

Chapter Eight

FALSE-SCORPIONS

CHELONETHI

False-scorpions or Chelonethi (= Pseudoscorpiones) are unmistakable animals on account of their *palps* which resemble lobster claws (figs. 90–94). They are all small; the largest is only about 4 mm. long, and the body is elongated and somewhat flat. There are 0, 2 or 4 eyes on the sides of the anterior part of the *cephalothorax*; as the number is an important diagnostic feature and the eyes are not always easy to see, it is essential to look for them with adequate light focused obliquely on to the animal. Other important points are the number and position of the tactile hairs or *trichobothria*. These are outstandingly long and fine, and even when one is accidentally lost the position of its insertion into the integument can be seen as a small ring. The *maxillae* are the two basal segments between the palps; in some species they are pitted or coarsely granulated. The *anterior median process*, when present, is a small tooth-like projection in the middle of the front edge of the cephalothorax. See figs. 95 and 104.

With care, most species can be determined when freshly killed in 70% alcohol. Alternatively, false-scorpions can be cleaned and mounted and the collection kept as a series of slides. It is preferable to use a cavity slide for mounting and polyvinol alcohol mountant is recommended, though Canada Balsam may also be used. A strong hand-lens or low-power microscope is essential for the examination of specimens.

These fascinating little creatures live in woodland litter, in moss

84

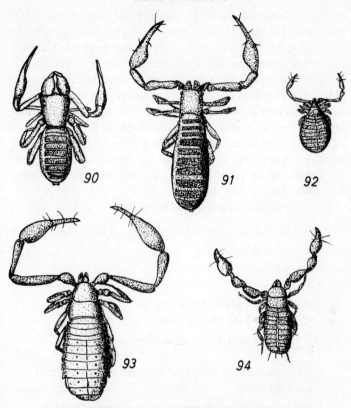

Examples of false-scorpion families
90. Chthoniidae; 91. Neobisiidae; 92. Cheiridiidae;
93. Cheliferidae; 94. Chernetidae. (From Cloudsley-Thompson, 1958)

and behind the bark of trees. Two species at least live on or near the seashore, and two others are sometimes found clinging to legs of harvest-spiders or flies; this appears to be a method of

85

dispersal. False-scopions are probably entirely carnivorous. So far as is known the eggs are laid in a small rounded cocoon spun by the female, and which in some species she appears to guard. There are 26 British species but until more records have been published it is difficult to know either how common some species are or to judge their distribution. Thirteen species are mentioned here. Of these, some may be mostly southern or western in their distribution, but search for false-scorpions is worth while in any part of Britain, as observations on their lives are much needed. Evans & Browning (1954) give an up-to-date account of the taxonomy of the British species and their biology is discussed by Cloudsley-Thompson (1958).

The commoner species may be keyed thus:

1. Body divided by a distinct longitudinal median line . 2
   Body not divided 10

2. No eyes. 3
   Eyes 2 8

3. Body shining, tibia 4 with a long hair . . . 4
   Body dull, no long hair on tibia 5

4. Hind tarsus with a long hair inserted in middle
                                   Lamprochernes godfreyi
   Hind tarsus with a long hair inserted about one-third
      from the base . . . . . . *L. nodosus*

5. Maxillae granulate underneath; front margin of free joint
      of chela with 1 tooth, no long hair on hind tarsus, 2
      long hairs on 11th abdominal segment   *Allochernes dubius*
   Maxillae scarcely or not granulate below; several teeth
      on front margin of free joint of chela . . . 6

6. Cephalothorax and palps honeycombed; no long hair on
      hind tarsus . . . . . . *Chernes cimicoides*
   Cephalothorax granulate; hind tarsus with long hair . 7

7. 2·6 mm. Palps dull . . . . *Toxochernes panzer*
   3·5 mm. Palps brilliantly shining . *Dendrochernes cyrneus*

8. 1·1–1·4 mm. Eyes not near front margin of cephalothorax; form somewhat rounded viewed from above
   Cheiridium museorum
   Longer than 1·1 mm. Eyes near front margin of cephalothorax; finger of chela larger than hand . . . 9

9. Tarsal claw with a tooth . . . *Chelifer cancroides*
   Tarsal claw without a tooth, near the coast often on sand dunes. . . . . *Dactylochelifer latreillei*

10. Anterior legs with tarsi 2-segmented 11
    Anterior legs with tarsi 1-segmented 12

11. Eyes 2: anterior median process of cephalothorax acute; mainly southern . . . . . *Roncus lubricus*
    Eyes 4; anterior median process of cephalothorax not or scarcely visible . . . . *Neobisium muscorum*

12. Posterior margin of cephalothorax with 4 bristles
    Chthonius ischnocheles
    Posterior margin of cephalothorax with 2 bristles; fingers of chelae straight and much longer than bulb
    C. tetrachelatus

Lamprochernes godfreyi (Kew) (fig. 95). Length: 1·6 mm. Body divided by median line; no eyes. Faintly granulate on parts of dorsum except anterior part of cephalothorax. Palps and cephalothorax reddish-brown, abdomen greenish-brown. On flies' legs, in moss and woodland litter; widely distributed.

L. nodosus (Schrank) (fig. 96). Length: 2 mm. or just under. Body divided by median line; no eyes. Cephalothorax weakly granulate at sides; abdomen not granulate. In plant refuse, manure heaps; also carried on flies.

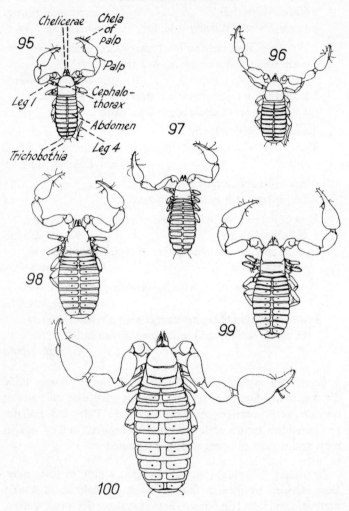

95
Chelicerae
Chela of palp
Palp
Cephalo-thorax
Abdomen
Leg 4
Leg 1
Trichobothia

96

97

98

99

100

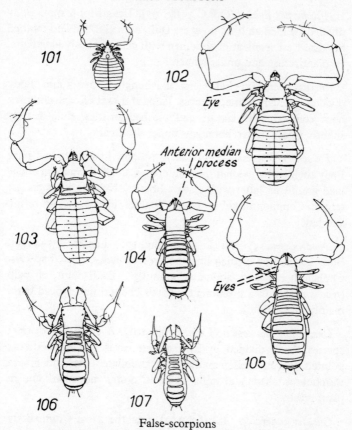

False-scorpions

95. *Lamprochernes godfreyi*; 96. *Lamprochernes nodosus*; 97. *Allochernes dubius*; 98. *Chernes cimicoides*; 99. *Toxochernes panzeri*; 100. *Dendrochernes cyrneus*; 101. *Cheiridium museorum*; 102. *Chelifer cancroides*; 103. *Dactylochelifer latreillei*; 104. *Roncus lubricus*; 105. *Neobisium muscorum*; 106. *Chthonius ischnocheles*; 107. *Chthonius tetrachelatus*. (After Kew, 1911)

Allochernes dubius (O.P.C.) (fig. 97). Length: 1·6 mm. Body divided by median line; no eyes. Dull, with clubbed and toothed bristles. Last segment of abdomen with conspicuously long hairs. In plant refuse and under stones.

Chernes cimicoides (Fab.) (fig. 98). Length: 2·2–2·7 mm. Body divided by median line; no eyes. Palps and part of cephalothorax honeycombed, with clavate and toothed bristles; dull or only slightly glossy. Often abundant under dead bark.

Toxochernes panzeri (C. L. K.) (fig. 99). Length: 2–2·5 mm. Body divided by median line; no eyes. Cephalothorax and abdomen granulate, latter with clavate bristles. No long hairs on last tergite. Common in old outhouses (stables, barns, etc.), in refuse and hay.

Dendrochernes cyrneus (L. Koch) (fig. 100). Length: 3·5–4 mm. Body divided by median line; no eyes. A dark-coloured species. Cephalothorax and abdomen granulate. Basal joint of palp (*trochanter*) with a prominent tubercle. Found under dead bark, mainly in the South.

Cheiridium museorum (Leach) (fig. 101). A small but distinct species; body divided by median line; eyes 2. Cephalothorax pointed, this and abdomen markedly granulate. Often indoors, in warehouses, sheds and mills, in birds' nests, under bark and in plant refuse.

Chelifer cancroides (L.) (fig. 102). Length: 2·6–4·5 mm. Body divided by median line; eyes 2. Cephalothorax darker than rest of body, strongly granulate. Abdomen with clavate hairs. First seven abdominal segments produced at sides into a backwardly directed tooth-like process. In old buildings, birds' nests, under bark, etc.

Dactylochelifer latreillei (Leach) (fig. 103). Length: 2–3 mm. Body divided by median line; eyes 2. A dark-coloured species.

Cephalothorax strongly granulate; abdomen finely granulate with short bluntish bristles. Common; maritime.

Roncus lubricus (L. Koch) (fig. 104). Length: 2·5–3 mm. Body not divided; eyes 2. Abdomen smooth or slightly reticulate at sides; hand and finger of palp granulated; tibia of palp smooth. Mainly in the south, in moss and on ground amongst sward.

Neobisium muscorum (Leach) (fig. 105). Length: 1·7–3 mm. Body not divided; eyes 4. Palpal finger much larger than hand; femur of palp smooth and distinctly stalked. Tubercle of movable finger of chelicera distinct. Widely distributed; in woodland litter, in moss and under stones.

Chthonius ischnocheles (Hermann) (fig. 106). Length: 1·6–2·4 mm. Body not divided; eyes 4. Cephalothorax markedly broader in front, with 20 to 24 conspicuous bristles, four of which are on the hind margin. Eyes conspicuous. Finger of palp much longer than hand. Widely distributed, mainly in plant refuse.

C. tetrachelatus (Prey.) (fig. 107). Length: 1·3–1·9 mm. Body not divided; eyes 4. Cephalothorax with 18 bristles, two of which are on the hind margin. Finger of palp longer than hand. Widely distributed, under stones, etc. Often abundant near the seashore.

REFERENCES

CLOUDSLEY-THOMPSON, J. L. (1958) *Spiders, scorpions, centipedes and mites*. London: Pergamon.

EVANS, G. O., and BROWNING, E. (1954) *Synopses of the British fauna No. 10 – Pseudoscorpiones*. London: Linn. Soc.

Chapter Nine

HARVEST-SPIDERS

OPILIONES

Harvest-spiders or Opiliones and true spiders (Araneae) are two distinct orders of the Arachnida. Some members of the Opiliones look rather like spiders, though the relationship is not very close and the resemblance is probably due more to convergence during the evolution of the two orders, rather than to morphological similarities. The Opiliones are an ancient and declining group; fossil harvest-spiders are known from the Carboniferous period – about 250 million years ago.

Harvest-spiders are carnivorous, feeding on small insects, worms, millipedes and the like when these blunder into their long legs. They are attracted to the entomologist's sugar patch, the bodies of dead animals and water, which they drink. Predatory insects, spiders and spiders' webs, and centipedes reduce their numbers and the highest mortality is probably in the young stages. They also have physical difficulties with which to contend in their environment; they are liable to rapid water-loss, which probably accounts for their general nocturnal activities. Their biology is discussed by Cloudsley-Thompson (1958).

Members of this order of the Arachnida are at once distinguishable from true spiders by:

(a) The complete union of *cephalothorax* and *abdomen* from side to side giving the body the appearance of being in one piece (fig. 108).

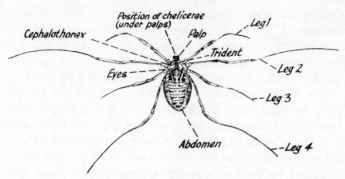

Diagnostic characters of harvest-spiders
108. *Oligolophus agrestis*

(b) The two eyes on top of the cephalothorax which are usually set on a small hummock – the *ocularium* (fig. 110).

(c) The absence of silk glands – no harvest-spider can produce silk.

(d) The two *odoriferous glands* (fig. 111) visible in most British species, one at each side near the front of the cephalothorax; these should not be mistaken for eyes.

(e) The fact that the second legs are the longest (a few British spiders also have legs of the second pair slightly longer than the others).

Harvest-spiders show different degrees of adaptation to habitat, chiefly in the length of legs and other structural characters, and in temperature and humidity preferences. Nearly all the 21 British species are widely distributed, and a number are familiar creatures of woodland and hedgerow towards the end of summer, when most of them become adult.

Only one of the three sub-orders into which the order is divided is represented in Britain. This is the **Palpatores.**

There are three British families. The most important is the

Phalangiidae which contains *Phalangium opilio* - the type genus and species. The two members of the Trogulidae are uncommon and live close to the ground where they are not easy to find. The two species of Nemastomatidae inhabit grassy places, living amongst the bases of plants, under logs and in similar places.

The British species are not difficult to identify and keys are given by Todd (1948) and Sankey (1956). The descriptions are those of the adults, but in most cases they apply also to immature individuals, at least in the last instar or so. Immature harvest-spiders have the *genital plate* sealed down (see fig. 114); in mature specimens the *penis* or *ovipositor* can usually be extruded from under the genital plate by gently squeezing the abdomen from the sides. The chief external characters are shown in fig. 108.

Family *Phalangiidae*

In these, the tip of the palp bears a claw. Tarsus of palp longer than tibia: second pair of legs considerably longer than length of body.

Homalenotus quadridentatus (Cuvier). Length: to about 5 mm. A rather flat, short-legged, brownish species, easily recognised by the four blunt 'teeth' projecting backwards from the apparent end of the abdomen – actually the fifth segment (fig. 109). Widely distributed, favouring soils overlying limestone: it lives under stones and at the base of sward plants.

Leiobunum spp. Species with exceptionally long legs and very small round bodies up to 4 mm. long. *L. blackwalli* (Meade) is distinguished from *L. rotundum* (Latr.) by the white ring round each eye which is lacking in the latter (figs. 110 & 111). Both are common in rank vegetation, though *L. rotundum* also occurs commonly on walls and tree-trunks, usually in shady places.

Mitopus morio (Fab.) (figs. 112 & 113). Length of body up to about 8 mm.; the male is usually smaller and darker. Both sexes

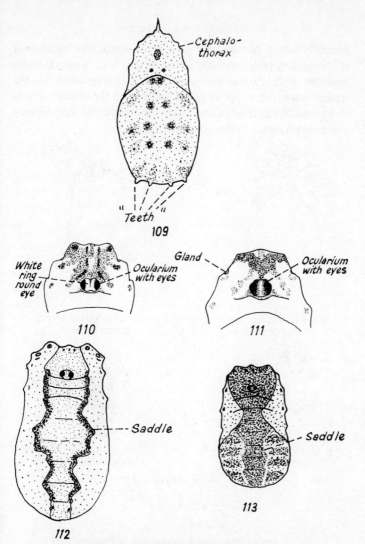

Diagnostic characters of harvest-spiders

109. *Homalenotus quadridentatus* body 'teeth'; 110. *Leiobunum blackwalli* ocularium with white rings; 111. *Leiobunum rotundum* ocularium without white rings; 112. *Mitopus morio* ♀ body showing saddle; 113. *Mitopus morio* ♂ body showing saddle

normally have a distinct hour-glass saddle-mark, but the amount of colour is variable especially in the female. This species is easily confused with *Phalangium opilio* but is distinguished by the widely spaced, short spines of the trident and the absence of two short denticles in front of and below the trident (fig. 120). A very common species in herbaceous vegetation.

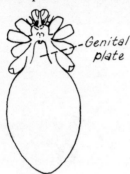

114. *Oligolophus agrestis* ventral view of body ♀

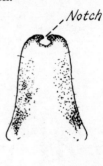

115. *Oligolophus agrestis* genital plate ♀

116. *Oligolophus tridens* body showing saddle

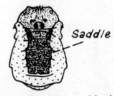

117. *Lacinius ephippiatus* body showing saddle

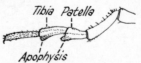

118. *Platybunus triangularis* left palp

Diagnostic characters of harvest-spiders

Oligolophus agrestis (Meade). Body length to about 6 mm. The female is the only British harvest-spider with a notched genital plate (figs. 114 & 115); in the male this has only a slight depression. Widespread on trees, bushes and among herbaceous vegetation.

O. tridens (C. L. K.) (fig. 116). Body length to about 6 mm. The male is usually smaller. A rather short-legged species, brownish and with a dark saddle. The spines of the trident are upright and the middle one is usually larger than the others. Common beneath herbaceous vegetation.

Lacinius ephippiatus (C. L. K.) (fig. 117). Body length to about 6 mm. with a very distinct dark saddle which is square at the end: mature in June and July. Amongst herbaceous vegetation.

Platybunus triangularis (Herbst). Body length to about 6 mm. A yellowish-brown species with long legs and with a conspicuous ocularium bearing two rows of eight or nine short spines. Patella and tibia of palp with *apophyses* (fig. 118). Mature in May or June. In herbaceous vegetation.

Phalangium opilio (L.) (fig. 119). Body length to about 8 mm. The two short denticles below the front edge of the cephalothorax (fig. 120) together with the white underside, are characteristic. The male has horns on the second joint of the chelicerae (fig. 121). Common and widespread, chiefly in low vegetation.

Opilio parietinus (Degeer). Body length to about 8 mm. Distinguished from *P. opilio* by the speckled underside and absence of denticles below the front edge of the cephalothorax (fig. 120), and lighter dorsal surface.

Family *Trogulidae*

Flattened, slow-moving species living close to the ground, often covered with earth particles. Second pair of legs scarcely longer than the body: front part of cephalothorax produced into a

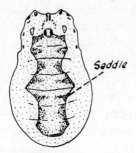

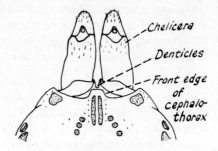

119. *Phalangium opilio* body showing saddle

120. *Phalangium opilio* front edge of cephalothorax

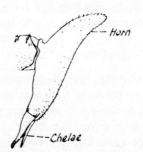

121. *Phalangium opilio* right chelicera with horn

Diagnostic characters of harvest-spiders

bifurcate hood which is often obscured by adhering earth. Two species: *Trogulus tricarinatus* (L.) (fig. 122) 7-9 mm. long and *Anelasmocephalus cambridgei* (Westwood) 3-4 mm. long. The former is confined to regions with strongly basic soils and the latter, though not restricted to such soils, appears to prefer them.

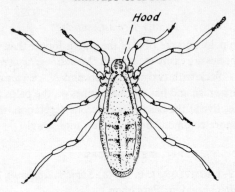

122. *Trogulus tricarinatus*

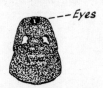

123. *Nemastoma lugubre* body

124. *Nemastoma chrysomelas* palp

Diagnostic characters of harvest-spiders

99

Family *Nemastomatidae*

No claw on palp, and the tibia of the palp is longer than its tarsus. The two species are easily recognised. *Nemastoma lugubre* (Müller) (fig. 123) is black with two white spots and *N. chrysomelas* (Hermann) is brownish and has clubbed spines on the palps (fig. 124). Both species live at the base of herbaceous vegetation, the former being the more common. Body about 3 mm. long.

REFERENCES

CLOUDSLEY-THOMPSON, J. L. (1958) *Spiders, scorpions, centipedes and mites.* London: Pergamon.

SANKEY, J. H. P. (1956) 'How to begin the study of Harvest-spiders'. *Countryside* (N.S.) **17,** 370–377.

TODD, V. (1948) 'Key to the determination of British Harvestmen. (*Arachnida, Opiliones*)'. *Ent. mon. Mag.* **84,** 109–113.

Chapter Ten

SPIDERS

ARANEAE

Spiders, or Araneae, form one of the most widely distributed and numerous of animal groups, both in species and in individuals. About 580 different kinds are found in Britain; there are nearly three times as many in France, and the world total has been estimated at over 30,000 species. Spiders of one kind or another can be found everywhere. Some are wandering hunters of the open grassland, others lurk under logs, stones or bark, in holes, on vegetation, in birds' nests, sheds and houses. Some hunt their prey by sight, others are nocturnal and find the insects and wood-lice on which they feed by the sense of touch. *Scytodes thoracica* (p. 108) entangles its prey in poison gum squirted from the rapidly vibrated jaws; *Atypus affinis* (p. 104) lives like a hermit in its silken 'purse-web', eating insects that happen to crawl across the exposed portion of the tube. Some spiders spin orb-webs or horizontal sheet-webs, others entangle their prey in silken snares of various intricate shapes and designs.

The biology of spiders has been described by many writers, and a number of excellent books by Bristowe (1939, 1941, 1958) and Savory (1928, 1952), among others, are listed in the references. (See also Cloudsley-Thompson, 1958.)

Most people are familiar with the garden spider, *Araneus diadematus* (p. 119), whose white cross made her an object of veneration in the Middle Ages. They also know the long-legged house-spiders, *Tegenaria* spp. (p. 115), which spin cobwebs in the corners of rooms and outhouses, and also perhaps the little black money-spiders of the family Linyphiidae whose autumnal spinning clothes the countryside in gossamer. Other kinds may be less conspicuous, although they are striking enough when discovered.

The general appearance of all spiders is much the same (figs.

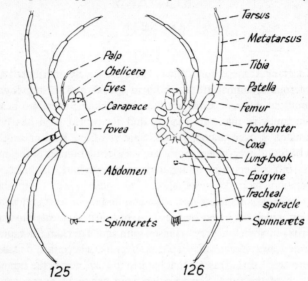

External features of a spider to show terminology
125. Dorsal view; 126. Ventral view. (After Locket & Millidge, 1951)

125 & 126). They are characterised by the presence of four pairs of walking legs, a body divided into two parts by a narrow waist or *pedicel*, abdominal *spinnerets* and *palpal organs* which, in males, are used for mating. The head usually bears eight eyes, although in some families the number is reduced to six. The jaws or *chelicerae* bear needle-like fangs at the apex whose poison paralyses and possibly aids in the digestion of the prey.

In front of the walking legs is a pair of leg-like appendages, the palps, referred to above. In adult males the terminal segment or tarsus of these is expanded to form a hollow organ for the storage of sperm, and is inserted into the female's body during mating. The shape and design of this palpal organ is often extremely complex and is used as a criterion for identification (figs. 155 & 156). Indeed, it is rarely possible to identify immature spiders with any certainty.

The external genitalia of female spiders, whose shape is also used in identification, is known as the *epigyne* (fig. 157). This too is exposed and developed only after the last moult and takes the form of complex chitinous plates just in front of a long groove or *epigastric furrow* on the anterior part of the ventral side of the abdomen. Behind the epigastric furrow can be seen a pair of *lung-books* which is used in respiration, and the abdomen terminates in six pairs of spinnerets which secrete the silk used in cocoon and web construction.

All spiders are carnivorous, feeding on a variety of insects, woodlice, 'myriapods', false-scorpions, harvest-spiders and other spiders. They are classified in a number of families, based on morphological characters which are often correlated with mode of life. Thus we have wolf-spiders (Lycosidae), ground hunters (Gnaphosidae and Clubionidae, figs. 130, 144, 145), nocturnal six-eyed Dysderidae, jumping-spiders (Salticidae), crab-spiders (Thomisidae), the Agelenidae which spin horizontal cobwebs, various families whose members weave different kinds of web-snares (Theridiidae, Argiopidae, Linyphiidae) and so on. The type of habitat in which a spider is found, and the kind of web it makes, are often useful guides to identification.

Many of the species which dwell on vegetation can be caught by means of a sweep net or by shaking branches over a beating tray. Ground-living species are most easily trapped in a glass or perspex tube, whilst those that occur in holes can sometimes be lured into the open by means of a piece of grass or a vibrating tuning-fork.

Spiders are best killed and preserved by placing them in a corked tube containing $70^0_{\ 0}$ alcohol or industrial methylated spirit to which $5^0_{\ 0}$ glycerol may be added. A label giving date, locality and other details written in pencil or indian ink should always be placed inside the tube with the specimen. Labels stuck on the outside are liable to come off and the memory should never be trusted in such matters. You have only to lay aside an interesting collection of animals and, when they are rediscovered, after weeks or months, all the necessary data will have been forgotten. Dim recollection gives no hint and joy turns to anger as the tube is shaken and turned round and round in a vain effort to see something which will suggest whence they came. Eventually the whole lot is consigned to the dustbin in disgust, for specimens without data are seldom worth keeping.

In the following pages are given descriptions of some of the larger and more common or striking of the British spiders. For the identification of other species the magnificent monograph by Locket & Millidge (1951, 1953) should be consulted. All descriptions given below are based on that work.

Family *Atypidae*

Chelicerae very massive, articulated vertically (in all other families they move laterally) (fig. 158). The fangs when folded at rest lie in a plane parallel to the axis of the body. There is one British species, *Atypus affinis* (Eichw.), the 'purse-web' spider (fig. 127), our only representative of the sub-order Mygalomorpha which includes the trap-door and 'bird-eating' spiders of the tropics. It usually lives in chalky districts in southern counties, and is unlikely to be confused with any other species. Great care must be taken in digging out the long tubular but inconspicuous web from the soil in which it is buried. The carapace (fig. 139) is greenish-brown in colour, the abdomen brown and clothed in short hairs.

Length: ♂ *c.* 8–9 mm., ♀ *c.* 12 mm.

Family *Dictynidae*

This family includes most of the British spiders which possess a *cribellum* and *calamistrum*. The cribellum (fig. 160) is a sieve-like plate immediately in front of the anterior spinnerets from which flocculent, sticky silk is combed on to the threads of the web by means of the calamistrum, a series of little curved spines on the upper margins of the metatarsi of the fourth pair of legs (fig. 159). Eight eyes and three tarsal claws are present. The webs are irregular with a peculiar texture and bluish colour, often to be seen on gateposts and fences. Three common British species occur, all of which can be found in holes in walls, in bark, under stones, flower-pots and fallen logs and not infrequently indoors.

Amaurobius (= *Ciniflo*) *ferox* (Walck.). A sinister, sombre-coloured, almost black spider with shining white eyes, *A. ferox* can easily be recognised in all stages of development. The adult male has a striking white palpal bulb, but is found during the autumn months only, whilst the female can be seen throughout the year.

Length: ♂ 8·5–10 mm., ♀ 11·5–15 mm.

Amaurobius similis (Bl.). General appearance similar to that of *A. ferox*, but the carapace is reddish-brown (fig. 140) and the abdomen has a more conspicuous pattern consisting of a dorsal median dark mark, wider behind than in front, flanked by light areas and followed by an oblong light region and then by a series of obscure darker chevrons. The legs are annulated.

Length: ♂ 6–8 mm., ♀ 9–12 mm.

Amaurobius fenestralis (Stroem). Similar to the above but

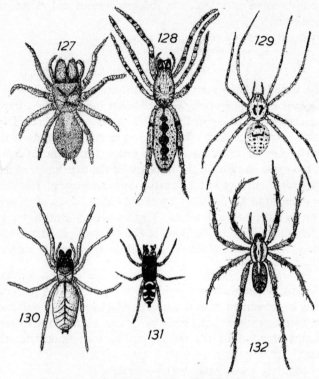

Examples of spider families

127. *Atypus* (Atypidae); 128. *Segestria* (Dysderidae);
129. *Scytodes* (Scytodidae); 130. *Clubiona* (Clubionidae);
131. *Salticus* (Salticidae); 132. *Lycosa* (Lycosidae).
(Mostly after Locket & Millidge, 1951, 1953)

smaller, with brighter colours. (The three species can usually be distinguished by their coloration, but recourse must be made to the appearance of the genitalia in cases of doubt.)

Length: ♂ 4·5–7 mm., ♀ 7–8 mm.

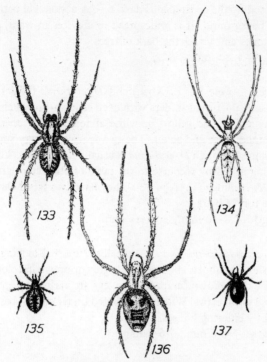

Examples of spider families

133. *Tegenaria* (Agelenidae); 134. *Tetragnatha* (Tetragnathidae); 135. *Theridion* (Theridiidae); 136. *Meta* (Argiopidae); 137. *Erigone* (Linyphiidae). (Mostly after Locket &
Millidge, 1951, 1953)

Family *Dysderidae*

Nocturnal hunting-spiders recognised by the presence of only *six*
eyes and the smooth carapace without any markings (fig. 141).
There is no epigyne.

Segestria senoculata (L.) (fig. 128). This species can at once be

107

recognised by the conspicuous dark zig-zag abdominal pattern on a light background. It is widespread in crevices in walls, among loose stones and under the bark of trees.

Length: 7–10 mm. ♂ & ♀.

Dysdera crocata (C. L. Koch) and *D. erythrina* (Walck.) (fig. 141). Large nocturnal spiders with deep reddish-brown chitinous portions and a pale yellow or white abdomen. Not uncommon under stones, logs and so on. The two species are very similar in appearance, although *D. erythrina* is usually the smaller. They can be distinguished by recourse to the table of characters given by Locket & Millidge (1951, p. 84). They have two tarsal claws and a dense tuft of hairs.

Length: ♂ 8–10 mm., ♀ 10–15 mm.

Harpactea hombergi (Scop.). A smallish, unusual-looking spider with a slender tubular abdomen, pale grey or brown in colour, and a narrow dark brown carapace. The legs are variegated and there are three tarsal claws. Widely distributed under stones, bark, etc., frequently entering houses.

Length: ♂ 5–6 mm., ♀ 6–7 mm.

Family *Scytodidae*

This family contains but a single species, the rare spitting-spider, *Scytodes thoracica* (Latr.). This six-eyed spider has a carapace unusually high posteriorly, very slender legs and a conspicuous pattern of black markings on a yellow background (figs. 129 & 142). It is sometimes to be seen on the ceilings of houses in southern counties where it catches its prey by squirting gum from the rapidly vibrating chelicerae.

Length: ♂ & ♀ 5–6 mm.

Family *Pholcidae*

Eyes, eight in number, legs extremely long and thin giving a general appearance closely resembling that of a harvest-spider.

Pholcus phalangioides (Fuess.) (figs. 138 & 143). A characteristic inhabitant of houses and sheds in southern England.

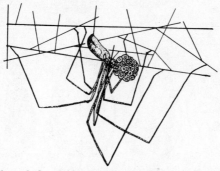

138. *Pholcus phalangioides* carrying an egg-sac in her chelicerae
(After Bristowe, 1958)

Family *Gnaphosidae*

A large family of nocturnal hunting-spiders. Eyes eight, in two rows, abdomen long and narrowish, usually without markings. Spinnerets (fig. 161) clearly projecting from the posterior end of the abdomen, the anterior ones distinctly separated (cf. Clubionidae, fig. 162). Tarsal claws, two. Most species are dull-coloured or black (*Zelotes* spp.), living under stones, leaves, bark, etc., where they build silken retreats.

Drassodes lapidosus (Walck.) (fig. 144). A large spider with a brownish carapace and mouse-grey abdomen. Widely distributed under stones and bark, etc.

Length: variable, 6–24 mm. (♂ usually smaller than ♀).

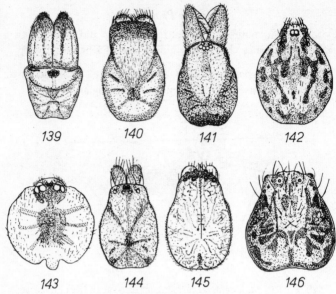

Spider carapaces

139. *Atypus* (Atypidae); 140. *Amaurobius* (Dictynidae);
141. *Dysdera* (Dysderidae); 142. *Scytodes*; 143. *Pholcus*
(Pholcidae); 144. *Drassodes* (Gnaphosidae); 145. *Clubiona*
(Clubionidae); 146. *Xysticus* (Thomisidae). (After Bristowe,
1958)

Herpyllus (= *Scotophaeus*) *blackwalli* (Thor.). (Figs. 155 and 156).
Similar in appearance to *D. lapidosus* but confined almost entirely
to houses. The carapace is narrower and the median eyes of the
anterior row are considerably larger than the laterals, a distinctive
character.

Length: ♂ 8–9 mm., ♀ 10–11 mm.

Family *Thomisidae*

Typical members of this family have a characteristic crab-like appearance, the carapace and abdomen being short and broad. The first two pairs of legs are stout and, in the genera *Xysticus*, *Oxyptila* and *Misumena*, etc., are much longer than the last two pairs; the spiders frequently run sideways like a crab. The spiders of this family lie in wait for their prey in flowers and vegetation. There are two tarsal claws.

Xysticus cristatus (Clerck) (fig. 146). This is the common crab-spider of vegetation and low herbage. The female has a mottled brown carapace with characteristic markings; the abdomen is pale with brown leaf-shaped central markings. The colours of the male are more contrasted.

Length: ♂ 4–5 mm., ♀ 6–7 mm.

Genus *Philodromus*

The species of this genus can be distinguished from *Xysticus* spp. by the fact that they are much less crab-like in appearance and the legs are approximately equal in length. The carapace is broader than long and relatively narrower in front; the eyes smaller and more uniform in size. The commonest species is *P. aureolus* (Clerck). The female is generally a dull reddish-brown in colour, with a characteristic pattern. The carapace has a yellow central band, the abdomen is yellowish in the centre with series of brown spots and chevrons. The male is darker with a metallic hue.

Family *Salticidae*

This family comprises the jumping-spiders – immediately recognisable on account of the massive, square-fronted carapace with four, large, forwardly directed eyes on its anterior edge. The four other eyes form a rectangle well behind the front of the carapace. The legs tend to be rather short for the spiders spin no snare but usually leap upon their prey. There are 32 British species included in 17 genera: the two most frequently encountered are described below.

Salticus scenicus (Clerck) (figs. 131 & 149). This is the well-known 'zebra spider', a familiar sight on sunny walls and buildings. The carapace is dark brown to black with two white blotches, the abdomen having the clear pattern illustrated in fig. 131.

Length: ♂ 5–6 mm., ♀ 5–7 mm.

Euophrys frontalis (Walck.). Of the jumping-spiders that inhabit vegetation and are caught in the sweep net, *E. frontalis* is undoubtedly the most common and widespread. It is yellow-brown in colour, the carapace being darker, the abdomen pale with longitudinal rows of black blotches. The legs, too, are pale and not annulated, but in adult males the first pair is darker.

Length: ♂ 2–3 mm., ♀ 3–5 mm.

Family *Lycosidae*

Wolf-spiders can at once be recognised by their typical shape and markings (fig. 132). The eyes are in three rows, the first containing four small eyes, the second row two larger eyes and the third is composed of two medium-sized eyes. The family is rather homogeneous and its sub-division into genera is not always easy. Only a few representative species are described below. A Lycosid claw is shown in fig. 163.

Genus *Lycosa*

Species of this genus can be recognised by the fact that the head is noticeably elevated with almost vertical sides. The *clypeus* or space between the anterior eyes and the front edge of the carapace is wide; at least twice the diameter of one of the anterior eyes (fig. 147). *Lycosa tarsalis* (Thor.) is widespread and abundant everywhere. It is the dominant species found on moors and mountains. Its colours are often somewhat darker than that of other Lycosidae, but precise identification depends upon a number of fine details and the form of the genitalia. *Lycosa monticola* (Clerck), *L. pullata* (Clerck), *L. nigriceps* (Thor.)

L. amentata (Clerck) and *L. lugubris* (Walck.) are all equally widespread and abundant. *L. amentata* females can usually be distinguished by the conspicuously annulated legs, *L. nigriceps* males by the dense black bars on the palpal tibiae and tarsi. For other taxonomic particulars the work of Locket & Millidge (1951) must be consulted.

Length: ♂ 4–6·5 mm., ♀ 4–8 mm.

Genus *Trochosa*

Wolf-spiders of this genus can be recognised by their large size and the sloping sides to the head and carapace which has a median light-coloured band.

Trochosa ruricola (Deg.) and *T. terricola* (Thor.) are both large and common. *T. ruricola* is olive-brown in colour with a yellowish dorsal abdominal stripe, whereas *T. terricola* is darker. It is reddish-brown in colour and the dorsal abdominal stripe is no lighter than its surroundings.

Length: *T. ruricola* ♂ 7·5–9 mm., ♀ 10–14 mm.
T. terricola ♂ 7–9 mm., ♀ 7·5–14 mm.

Genus *Pirata*

At first sight the spiders of this genus resemble *Lycosa* spp. but the carapace has sloping sides and is characteristically marked with a backwardly pointing V.

Pirata hygrophilus (Thor.) is very widespread and by no means confined to marshy places. In our experience it can usually be recognised in the field by the greyish appearance of the abdomen. It tends to be smaller than the more rare members of the genus.

Length: ♂ 4·5–5·5 mm., ♀ 5–6·5 mm.

Family *Pisauridae*

The spiders of this family are somewhat similar in appearance to the Lycosidae but can be distinguished by their large size,

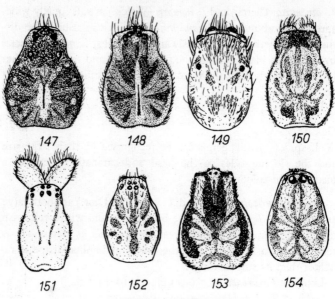

Spider carapaces

147. *Lycosa* (Lycosidae); 148. *Pisaura* (Pisauridae);
149. *Salticus* (Salticidae); 150. *Tegenaria* (Agelenidae);
151. *Tetragnatha* (Tetragnathidae); 152. *Theridion* (Theridiidae); 153. *Araneus* (Argiopidae); 154. *Linyphia* (Linyphiidae). (After Bristowe, 1958)

tapering abdomen and the fact that the second row of eyes is shorter than the third.

Pisaura mirabilis (Clerck) (fig. 148). This large and common species can easily be recognised by its shape and the fact that the female carries her egg cocoons in her jaws. The carapace is red-brown with a narrow, yellow, central stripe, the abdomen brown and hairy with a darker central pattern.

Length: ♂ c. 12 mm., ♀ 12–15 mm.

SPIDERS

Dolomedes fimbriatus (Clerck). A very large and striking spider, having a deep brown carapace with yellow edges continued as stripes along the sides of the abdomen. A widespread but local species, found only in swamps and marshes.

Length: ♂ 9–13 mm., ♀ 13–20 mm.

Family *Agelenidae*

The long-legged house-spiders of the genus *Tegenaria* (figs. 133 & 150) are so well known that lengthy description is unnecessary. Other members of the family Agelenidae can generally be recognised by their similar appearance, and especially by the length of the posterior spinnerets which are clearly larger than the anterior ones and stick out behind the abdomen of the spider (fig. 164). In the small spiders of the genus *Hahnia* the spinners are in a transverse row (fig. 165). There are eight eyes in three rows, not greatly unequal in size, and three toothed tarsal claws. This family includes the well-known water-spider *Argyroneta aquatica* (Clerck), which may be locally abundant in ponds and ditches throughout the British Isles.

Tegenaria domestica (Clerck). This is perhaps the most common of all our house-spiders. It is smaller than the two following species, and can be distinguished by the abdominal pattern which consists of dark sooty patches in a light background, giving a chequer-board appearance. Sometimes the pattern is indiscernible.

Length: ♂ 6–9 mm., ♀ 9–10 mm.

T. atrica (C. L. Koch). This common species has an abdominal pattern consisting of a median light longitudinal area flanked by a series of light and dark bars. It is considerably larger than *T. domestica* and can be distinguished from *T. parietina* by the absence of a reddish-brown abdominal streak.

Length: ♂ 13–14 mm., ♀ 11–15 mm.

T. parietina (Fourc.). Specimens of this species are usually

155. Male palp of *Herpyllus*   156. Female palp of *H.*
blackwalli   *blackwalli* for comparison

157. Epigyne of *Drassodes lapidosus*
Reproductive organs of spiders

somewhat larger than *T. atrica* and can be recognised by a reddish-brown streak running down the centre of the abdomen, whose pattern is less well defined than in *T. atrica*.

Length: ♂ *c.* 11 mm., ♀ *c.* 14 mm.

Agelena labyrinthica (Clerck) (fig. 164). This species looks very much like a house-spider, but it occurs outdoors on grass, heather or gorse on which it spins a large sheet-web with a tubular retreat. The abdomen is dark grey with a lighter mottled longitudinal region and a series of lighter transverse bars on either side of this. Mature in July and August.

Length: ♂ 8–9 mm., ♀ 8–12 mm.

Textrix denticulata (Oliv.). A pretty little spider that looks at first sight rather like a wolf-spider, except for its long, tapering projecting spinnerets. The abdominal pattern consists of a reddish median band with notched edges containing a reddish stripe

116

flanked by dark patches in its anterior half. Widely distributed under stones, bark and in vegetation.

Length: ♂ & ♀ 6–7 mm.

Family *Theridiidae*

Spiders of the family Theridiidae (figs. 135, 152) build webs with an irregular criss-cross structure and no clearly developed sheet. Their shapes are variable but, in general, they are less robust than orb-web spinners of the family Agelenidae and their abdomens more globular. Eyes eight, tarsal claws three, not hidden by tufts of hairs. The tarsi of the fourth legs bear a characteristic row of serrated bristles (fig. 167). Most species are small and not easily identified.

Steatoda bipunctata (L.). A common inhabitant of houses and sheds with a shining chocolate-brown abdomen, bright eyes and rather short legs.

Length: ♂ 4–5 mm., ♀ 4·5–7 mm.

Theridion denticulatum (Walck.). This and the next are perhaps the commonest species occurring on bushes and trees as well as indoors. The abdomen is black or grey with a variable pattern and a conspicuous triangular mark ventrally.

Length: ♂ 2·25–3·75 mm., ♀ 2·5–3·75 mm.

T. ovatum (Clerck). In this species the abdomen either has a pair of wide longitudinal carmine stripes, or is creamy white with four or five pairs of black spots. Widely distributed in low vegetation, especially nettles.

Length: ♂ 3–4 mm., ♀ 5–5·5 mm.

Family *Tetragnathidae*

The more common species of this family can be recognised by their elongated bodies and very long legs. The eight eyes are in

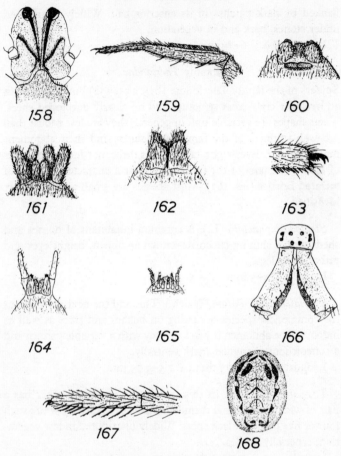

Diagnostic features of spiders

158. *Atypus affinis*, chelicerae and fangs; 159. *Amaurobius* fourth leg showing calamistrum; 160. *Amaurobius* cribellum and spinnerets; 161. *Drassodes* spinnerets; 162. *Clubiona* spinnerets; 163. Lycosid claws; 164. *Agelena labyrinthica*, spinnerets; 165. *Hahnia* spinnerets; 166. *Tetragnatha extensa*, chelicerae; 167. *Theridion* fourth tarsus; 168. *Zygiella x-notata*, abdomen. (After Locket & Millidge, 1951, 1953)

two rows and not greatly unequal in size; the chelicerae are unusually large and have extremely strong teeth (fig. 166).

Tetragnatha extensa (L.) (figs. 134 & 151). This widespread and abundant species is frequently taken in the sweep net from grass, reeds and bushes especially close to water. The carapace is yellowish with darker radiations from the centre, whilst the abdomen is usually pale green with a metallic sheen and a few darker chevrons from the central line.

Length: ♂ 6–9 mm., ♀ 8–11 mm.

Family *Argiopidae*

Orb-web spiders can usually be recognised by the flat carapace (fig. 153) and large, often circular abdomen. The eyes are not very dissimilar in size and there are three tarsal claws. There are over 40 British species, many of which are far from uncommon. Here we describe only the best known and most easily recognised.

Araneus diadematus (Clerck). This well-known garden-spider can always be recognised by the brown carapace and abdomen which bears a white central cross. It is found all over the British Isles on trees, low bushes and window-frames, reaching adulthood in the autumn months.

Length: ♂ 4·5–8 mm., ♀ 10–12 mm.

Araneus quadratus (Clerck). An even larger species than the last, with an abdomen of variable colour but characteristically reddish-brown with four impressed spots.

Length: ♂ 6–8 mm., ♀ 9–15 mm.

Araneus umbraticus (Clerck). Another large species whose flattened abdomen enables it to hide underneath loose bark from which it rarely emerges during the daytime. It can easily be identified by its curious flat appearance and dark colours.

Length: ♂ 8–9 mm., ♀ 11–14 mm.

Araneus cucurbitinus (Clerck). This small species can be recognised by its bright green abdomen which has a few black spots on its posterior half. It is common on trees and bushes all over the British Isles, being adult in early summer.

Length: ♂ 3·5–4 mm., ♀ 4–6 mm.

Meta segmentata (Clerck) (fig. 136). A very common species of trees and bushes recognised by its abdominal pattern, *M. segmentata* reaches maturity in late summer and autumn. Spiders of the genus *Meta* can be distinguished from *Araneus* spp. by the fact that the maxillae are longer than broad.

Length: ♂ 5–6 mm., ♀ 5–8 mm.

Zygiella x-notata (Clerck). This and its congeneric species build webs with one segment missing, and a line in the middle of this region leads from the centre of the web to the spider's retreat. *Z. x-notata* is usually greyish in colour with the characteristic abdominal pattern shown in fig. 168. Common in vegetation, window-frames and garden sheds.

Length: ♂ 3·5–5 mm., ♀ 6–6·5 mm.

Family *Linyphiidae*

This large family includes more than 250 British species and its members can be distinguished mainly by the absence of the characters delineating other families. Many species are small black 'money-spiders' whose identification is far from easy. Indeed, the family represents one of the 'specialist' groups referred to in the introduction. Linyphiid spiders spin webs in the form of a sheet which may or may not have lines above it: the spider lives underneath. Most species are ground-living, inhabiting moss and low vegetation. Others occur under stones, bark and fallen leaves. There are eight eyes, three tarsal claws and the chelicerae usually have stridulating ridges on them. Fig. 154 shows the carapace of *Linyphia*. The Linyphiidae can be divided into two sub-families: Linyphiinae in which the tibiae of the fourth legs bear two dorsal spines, and the Erigoniae (fig. 137) in which the fourth tibiae have a single spine. Locket & Millidge (1953) must be consulted for further details of classification.

REFERENCES

BRISTOWE, W. S. (1939, 1941) *The comity of spiders*. I, II. London: Ray. Soc.

BRISTOWE, W. S. (1958). *The world of spiders*. London: Collins.

CLOUDSLEY-THOMPSON, J. L. (1958) *Spiders, scorpions, centipedes and mites*. London: Pergamon.

LOCKET, G. H., and MILLIDGE, A. F. (1951, 1953) *British spiders*. I, II. London: Ray. Soc.

SAVORY, T. H. (1928) *The biology of spiders*. London: Sidgwick & Jackson.

SAVORY, T. H. (1945) *The spiders and allied orders of the British Isles*. London: Warne.

SAVORY, T. H. (1952) *The spiders web*. London: Warne.

Chapter Eleven

MITES AND TICKS

ACARI

Except for some species which trouble man, plague his crops and animals, or destroy his stored produce, the Acari (= Acarina) or mites and ticks are a comparatively little known group. Most of them are small and need special methods for their collection, such as a Berlèse or Tullgren funnel (Sankey, 1958). Except for *Ixodes*, the species mentioned here are not more than about 2 mm. in body length when adult; some are a good deal less and a × 10 lens or binocular microscope is needed to study most mites. Mites are widespread and occur in many kinds of habitat. They are often abundant in plant litter and in the soil where they form a very important element of the invertebrate fauna; in some grasslands it has been estimated that there are as many as 500 million per acre. They also occur on many plants, in or on which some are parasites. Certain of them are of well-known economic importance. Large numbers of the Acari are parasites of animals; some on the various groups of vertebrates and fewer on invertebrates. Others prey on invertebrates and some use them, as well as some vertebrates, as a travelling agency – a phenomenon known as *phoresy*. They also live in freshwater and in the sea.

The external anatomy of the Acari is very diverse and in some cases almost bizarre. The largest Acarines are the ticks which, after a meal of blood, may exceed the size of a small pea. The distinction between cephalothorax and abdomen is obscure but there is usually a well-developed head region, the *gnathosoma* or *capitulum* (fig. 169). Few species show obvious traces of external segmentation and the anal aperture is usually a vertical slit which distinguishes mites from young harvest-spiders in which it is horizontal. There are usually four pairs of legs in the adults (two pairs in all mites). The sensory *palps* lie immediately in front of the first pair of legs and the basal segment of the palp usually surrounds the *chelicerae*. The rest of the body forms the *idiosoma* whose upper surface is covered with hairs of various forms and degrees of density (see figs. 169 & 175). The idiosoma may be divided into an anterior *propodosoma* and a posterior *hypersoma* (= *hysterosoma*). After a few mites have been examined it is usually possible to recognise a member of this order even without a hand-lens.

There are probably more than 1700 British species of Acari and specific identification of the group is difficult. For critical examination specimens are best stored in 70% alcohol to which about 5% by volume of glycerine has been added. It is usually necessary to make a cleared microscope mount in a cavity slide. 70% lactic acid may be used and the slide with the specimen on it slightly warmed to hasten clearing. If it is necessary to make the exoskeletal parts more visible by staining, a mixture having the following formula is useful and will also clear the specimen: lactic acid 60 parts, glycerine 40 parts, with lignin pink added till the liquid is a bright cherry red. Mites may also be mounted in gum chloral (de Faure's medium). Details of methods are given by Evans *in* Kevan (1955) and by Wagstaffe & Fidler (1953).

Much remains to be discovered about the life-cycles of mites. In most species a six-legged larva hatches from the egg and there may be four active instars before the adult stage is reached, but this number is often reduced. In the Mesostigmata there is a larval and two nymphal stages (the proto- and deutonymph) before the mite matures. In the Metastigmata these are reduced to the larval and one nymphal stage. The two same stages occur in most of the Prostigmata in which the larva is often parasitic on animals. The Astigmata usually have a larval and two nymphal stages, but under unfavourable conditions a non-feeding *hypopus* may be produced as an additional stage between the first and second nymph; this has small ventral suckers by which it attaches itself to insects for transportation and dispersal. In addition to the larval form the Cryptostigmata have three nymphal stages – the third being called the *tritonymph*. Some stages in mites are parasitic on animals and plants for only part of their lives and are otherwise free-living.

Cloudsley-Thompson (1958) reviews the biology of this group and cites some important taxonomic works. Hughes (1959) gives a general account of the group with a very full bibliography; this work and that of Baker & Wharton (1952) are recommended for those who wish to specialise in the group.

The British representatives of the Acari are divided into five sub-orders:

(1) The Mesostigmata (= Parasitiformes)

These mites occur in the ground, in plant litter and occasionally in moss: some feed on decaying vegetable matter, others are parasites occurring on invertebrates (e.g. bumble-bees, dor beetles) and vertebrates; they are also found in the nests of bumble-bees and mammals.

There is one pair of breathing pores (*stigmata*): each opens as a small pit on the side of the body below the dorsal shield, just above the fourth pair of legs and near *coxae* 2, 3 and 4. The last, or tarsal segment of the palp has a forked or three-pronged hair on its inner basal angle. There is usually a tube-like structure, the *peritreme*, which extends anteriorly and sometimes posteriorly from the stigmata. The chelicerae usually bear chelae resembling lobster-claws, though these may be modified in parasitic species in which they may be more conspicuous in the male.

Among the Mesostigmata are a number of families which are largely exoparasites of animals. The Laelaptidae which occur on vertebrates and invertebrates sometimes occur in the nests of squirrels, mice and voles, whereas the Phytoseiidae occur chiefly on plants where they are probably predators on other small invertebrates. The Uropodidae live mainly in damp places where they feed on fungi and vegetable matter; some attach themselves to an insect host by a thread stalk secreted by glands in the anal region (genus *Uropoda*); they are slow-moving and are often common in humus, manure heaps and in moss. Amongst the Gamasides (a division of the Mesostigmata to which the Parasitidae belong) are many insect parasites which are sometimes found in woodland litter, rotting logs and other organic matter. They are without eyes, the legs are hairy and bear two claws. Leg 2 is thicker, leg 1 in males is antenna-like and sensory. *Parasitus fucorum* (Degeer) often occurs on bumble-bees (*Bombus* spp.) and on the related cuckoo-bees (*Psithyrus* spp.). The prostigmatic mite *Scutacarus* may be found attached to these parasites. *Pergamassus* spp. are commonly found in organic material, especially in the ground. *Parasitus* spp. are often abundant on dor beetles (*Geotrupes* spp.).

(2) **Metastigmata** (= **Ixodides**) Ticks

Ectoparasitic mites feeding on the blood of vertebrates; many species attach themselves to the host only for a short time and are therefore often found in litter and at the base of herbaceous sward and in moss, etc. Their most characteristic feature is a harpoon-like structure, the *hypostome*, which has recurved teeth and lies ventrally between the coxae of the palps (fig. 170). There are two stigmata; one on each side of the body situated just above and anterior to, or behind, coxa 4.

The Metastigmata, amongst other parasites, contains the mites of the genus *Ixodes*. *I. hexagonus* (Leach) commonly occurs on hedgehogs as well as other mammals. It is usually oval and is provided with a tough, hard and, in the female, extensible skin.

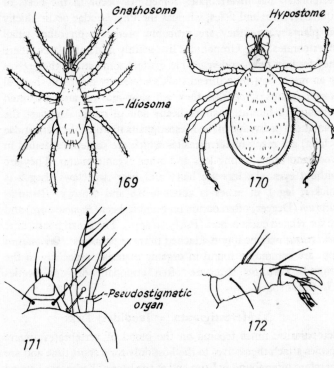

169. *Scirus longirostris* Hermann, a member of the Prostigmata. Length about 0·5 mm; 170 *Ixodes ricinus* ♂ (after Vitzthum, 1931). 171. Pseudostigmatic organ of a Cryptostigmatic mite (by courtesy of Dr G. O. Evans); 172. Thumb-claw complex of a Protostigmatic mite. (After Grandjean, 1946)

I. ricinus (L.) (fig. 170) is the common sheep tick. The female *Ixodes* sucks the blood of its host. The Argasidae are a related family, with three British species; in this family there is no dorsal scutum or hardened area.

(3) **Cryptostigmata** (= **Sarcoptiformes**) Beetle mites

Live in soil, plant litter, moss, etc. Mostly small, 0·5–1 mm. Adults often with strongly thickened integument and no external segmentation. Front part of the prosoma dorsally with two clubbed or pilose *pseudostigmatic organs* which arise from cup-like *pseudostigmata* (fig. 171). *Hypersoma* often with well-developed blade or wing-like expansions. Genital and anal apertures covered by paired valves. Stigmata often hidden or may be absent and respiration may take place through special porous areas of the cuticle on the hysterosoma and legs.

The Cryptostigmata are represented by a large number of families. The Oribatidae are dark-coloured, shiny, hard-skinned mites with the front of the body often produced into a broad plate; the palps are large. These animals sometimes occur in great numbers in soil, moss and plant litter, especially in woodlands. Mention should also be made here of the well-known cheese-mites, or Tyroglyphidae; see p. 130.

(4) **Astigmata**

Free-living, often in cereals, or parasitic. No stigmata or *tracheae* (air-tubes which ramify throughout the body). Limits of coxae of legs indicated by sub-cuticular sclerotised (hardened) bars of *apodemes*. Tibiae 1 and 2 have long and whip-like chaetae dorsally. Palps small and unmodified. Dorsal chaetae often long, except in parasitic species.

The Analgesidae are feather-inhabiting mites. Legs 3 and 4 often well developed. The same sub-order includes the Sarcoptidae or itch-mites; these are round, with short, bristly legs. Sarcoptidae are common parasites of some mammals and birds, often occurring on the legs of the latter. The itch or mange in man is caused by *Sarcoptes scabei* (L.) burrowing into the skin. (The irritation frequently felt after sitting on dry pasture towards the end of summer, however, is attributable to *Trombicula autumnalis* (Shaw) of the Prostigmata – see p. 130.) The Listrophoridae inhabit the hair of small mammals and only rarely occur in birds' feathers. *Glycyphagus domesticus* (Degeer) of the family Glycyphagidae sometimes abounds in houses, but it also occurs out of doors.

(5) **Prostigmata (= Trombidiformes)**

Free-living, some predatory, few parasitic; many feed on plants; some with an elongated and ringed body. Stigmata when present constitute one pair; each is situated above or near the first pair of legs at the base of the gnathosome and often associated with

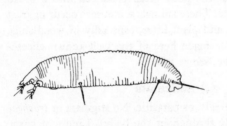

173. *Eriophyes ribis*. (After Hughes, 1959)

174. *Eriophyes avellanae*

peritremes. Usually without *apodemes*, but if these are present, then the hyperstome has overlapping dorsal plates (Tarsonemid mites). Without whip-like chaetae dorsally on tibia 1 and 2. Tibia and tarsus of palp often forming a thumb-claw complex (fig. 172). Chelicerae well developed or small and hidden. (See fig. 169).

The Prostigmata includes some well-known mites. The family Eriophyidae form plant galls and are recognisable by their elongate form and by having only two pairs of legs. Some cause swelling of buds, for example, the big-bud mites of black currants and hazels, *Eriophyes ribis* (Westwood) and *E. avellanae* (Nalepa), (figs. 173 & 174). The members of the Erythraeidae most often noticed are larvae of *Erythraeus* spp. These are reddish mites often seen clinging to the bodies of various butterflies of the family Satyridae (meadow brown, heaths, etc.). The Trombidiidae are large brownish or brilliant scarlet velvet mites inhabiting dryish places such as chalk downland sward; the larvae parasitise arthropods.

Pyemotes ventricosus (Newport) of the family Pyemotidae causes hay or grain itch when the mite turns from its usual role of an insect parasite to attack men handling stored grain; the adult mite attacks the larvae and pupae of grain moths. Amongst the Tetranychidae, *Tetranychus urticae* (Koch) – the red-spider mite – is a well-known pest of hot-houses and *Metatetranychus ulmi* (Koch) – the fruit-tree red-spider mite – sometimes causes great damage to apple and plum trees by sucking the sap from the

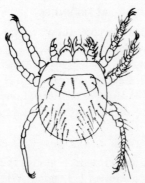

175. *Trombicula autumnalis* larva. (After Vitzthum, 1931)

foliage and covering it with a fine web. The related *Tetranychus lintearius* (Dufour) occurs on gorse and *T. tilearium* (Herm.) on limes. *Bryobia praetiosa* (Koch) – the clover mite – of the same family, is normally found on grass and low plants, but occasionally swarms in great numbers in houses. The Tarsonemidae, which have the hind legs ending in a whip-like seta, contains some well-known plant pests. *Tarsonemus fragariae* (Zimm.) lives on strawberries. Species of the genus *Cheyletus* prey on Tyroglyphid mites, some of which, e.g. *Tyroglyphus siro* (L.), are very destructive to insect collections. *Riccardoella limacum* (Schrank), family Ereynetidae, may often be seen moving actively on large slugs. *Scutacarus acarorum* (Goeze) has been referred to previously in connection with *Parasitus* (p. 125). Finally, mention must be made of *Trombicula autumnalis* (Shaw) – the harvest mite. The larva is six-legged (fig. 175) and is orange-coloured and barely visible to the naked eye; it normally attaches itself to a small mammal but occasionally to man into whose skin it injects a fluid which often has an irritant effect, especially in places where the clothing is tight against the skin and on the ankles and wrist.

REFERENCES

BAKER, E. W., and WHARTON, G. W. (1952) *An introduction to acarology*. New York: Macmillan.

CLOUDSLEY-THOMPSON, J. L. (1958) *Spiders, scorpions, centipedes and mites*. London: Pergamon.

HUGHES, T. E. (1959) *Mites, or the Acari*. London: Athlone Press.

KEVAN, D. K. McE. (editor) (1955) *Soil zoology*. London: Butterworth.

SANKEY, J. (1958) *Guide to field biology*. London: Longmans.

WAGSTAFFE, R. E., and FIDLER, J. H (1957) *The preservation of natural history specimens*, I. London: Witherby.

Chapter Twelve

SLUGS AND SNAILS

GASTROPODA

The dislike which most people feel for slugs and snails seems attributable to their sliminess as well as the depredations on garden and farm crops, of which, however, less than half a dozen of about 108 British species are guilty. Of the five classes of the phylum Mollusca, only one – the Gastropoda, has succeeded in establishing itself on dry land, but this constitutes an ecologically important group.

Certain species are sensitive to the amount of available calcium in their habitat (some calcium is needed for the shell), and occur only on soils in which this is relatively great. Many species inhabit places with a fairly constant high relative humidity, while a few thrive in quite dry places, though they are only active when the vegetation is wet. Many Gastropods live from twelve to eighteen months; and since none can move quickly, it is easier to observe them and study their ecology than is the case with most other invertebrates.

Slugs and snails are characterised by a number of well-marked external and internal features. The more important external features are (see figs. 176 & 193):

(a) Two pairs of hollow retractable tentacles at the anterior end of the body; the front ones bear organs of smell, the hind ones have eyes, except in the Pectinibranchia which have one pair of tentacles with eyes at the base, (see p. 136).

(b) The eyes, which appear as black specks at the tips of the longer tentacles.

(c) A muscular foot by which the animal moves. A pedal gland opens at the upper anterior end of the foot just below the mouth and discharges mucus which acts as a lubricant between the sole of the foot and the substratum over which the animal crawls. The slime gives an acid reaction, suggesting that it may help in burrowing at the beginning of hibernation when the snail enters

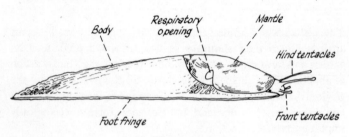

176. *Limax maximus*

the earth, especially in the alkaline soils on which the land Gastropods are usually most numerous. There are also other mucus glands on the skin which serve for protection against enemies and excessive evaporation.

(d) The respiratory opening leading from the lung cavity on the right side.

(e) The mouth, situated below the tentacles. There is a mobile, sensitive upper lip which may be well lobed, as in *Arion ater*. The upper and inner part of the mouth is chitinised and forms a hard base against which the file-like radula works when rasping and tearing fresh or decomposing plant material.

(f) All British land Gastropods, with the exception of the Streptoneura, are hermaphrodite.

(g) The majority of the land Gastropods have a spirally coiled shell (snails). In most slugs this is reduced to a few calcareous granules or a thin plate hidden beneath the *mantle*.

Land Gastropoda are found in most habitats but are scarce in more acid areas. They abound where humus has collected and in places offering shelter under accumulations of brushwood, grass and other material, in cracks in walls or tree-trunks, under stones, in marshy spots and places of more constant and generally high relative humidity. They live at the base of the sward, in moss, in sand dunes and in woodland litter. Some burrow into the soil and a few live there more or less permanently. Most hibernate in the soil or well-hidden cracks in rocks or under stones.

Snails, with two exceptions (which are operculate, p. 135), secrete a mucous *epiphragm* over the opening of the shell (the *aperture*). This shuts off the animal from external conditions, though the epiphragm is permeable to air even when highly calcified. The epiphragm may be thin and may function for a short duration only, as in periods of summer drought. Snails can, therefore, withstand wider climatic extremes than can slugs. Their distribution is also determined by the availability of calcium and suitable humus or other plant material for food, as well as by suitable relative humidity. Some Gastropod populations are modified by their natural enemies. Birds, some mammals, reptiles and amphibia and perhaps even man (especially in cultivated areas) are the more important biotic factors which regulate their numbers, though the young stages and eggs probably fall prey to such invertebrates as ground beetles (Carabidae), rove beetles (Staphylinidae), centipedes and other predators.

The eggs are laid in moist places, often in the earth. In most species the young hatch directly from the eggs, though in five British species the young snails hatch within the oviduct of the parent and are fully active when they leave the body.

The young Gastropod bears a general resemblance to the adult, though in those species which have a well-developed shell this is often more transparent and has fewer whorls. Identification of young stages requires experience and it is best first to become familiar with the adults. A few species, especially some members of the Zonitidae, are difficult to identify even when adult; for such groups a type collection of different stages, checked by an experienced collector, is invaluable.

Larger species may be collected directly or by putting on the ground traps such as pieces of wood, cloth or folded newspaper. Warm, damp conditions are best and the late evening is a good time. The smaller species are more easily found by bringing home bags of litter, flood débris, moss and loose earth, and sorting these on a table with the help of a wide-mesh sieve and a light suspended above. Tins and plastic bags can be used for collecting, and corked specimen tubes are useful for the smaller species.

Gastropods can be killed by drowning in cold water which has been boiled to drive off the air. They must be immersed in a container which is filled to the top and then tightly corked. They will then die extended, which is an advantage both for extracting them from their shells and for dissection which, in a few cases, is necessary for specific identification. The soft parts as well as the entire bodies of slugs may be preserved in 70% alcohol. Excessive slime can usually be removed by carefully wiping the specimen with a cloth. Preservation in 1% propylene phenoxetol, which retains the organs in a soft condition, is also worth trying. Specimens must first be preserved in any of the usual fixatives. The shells can be dried by dipping in alcohol and placing them on a piece of cloth or blotting-paper; further treatment is unnecessary.

The shell is made largely of calcium carbonate; in a few species it is mostly horny. White varities (albinos) sometimes occur; many are subject to variation in colour and pattern. A thickened lip usually indicates maturity. 'Teeth', which are thicker parts of the lip, are present in some species. If the aperture is on the right of the shell when this is held towards the observer, the shell is said to be *dextral*; if the aperture is on the left, the shell is *sinistral*. Only rarely is the normal position reversed in a particular species. The shell is covered with a thin outer layer of *periostracum* which, in old and weathered shells, may be worn away. The main part of the whorls and lip are formed of crystals of calcium carbonate (the *ostracum*) which may be coloured. The ostracum and periostracum are secreted by the mantle only at the growing edge of the shell. The thin, inner, mother-of-pearl layer (*nacreous* layer) is secreted last, and is used to repair the shell at any point. It can be seen inside the aperture.

For identification the snail shell is orientated as in fig. 193 with the aperture towards the observer. In species in which the shell is much flattened, the breadth (the broadest part of the shell) may exceed the height, which is measured from the apex of the spire to the lowermost part of the *bodywhorl*. The number of *whorls*, their sculpturing and colour and relationship of position to each other, as well as the position and shape of the mouth or aperture are important diagnostic features. The *columella* is the axis of the spire; and its central hollow cavity, unless filled in, is called the *umbilicus*. The latter may be deep and narrow, or shallow and wide, according to the arrangement of the whorls.

The taxonomic features of slugs are best seen in the living animal. The position of the *respiratory opening* in relation to the front and back edges of the mantle is important (fig. 176). The colour of the tentacles, the sole and its edge and of the slime, as well as the pattern made by the 'sculpturing' on the mantle and body, should be noted before preservation.

The British land Gastropods include two groups:

1. Shell spirally wound and closed by an *operculum*.[1] One pair of tentacles with eyes at base. All unisexual (except

[1] The *operculum* is a chitinous or calcareous 'door' attached permanently to the foot and fitting into the aperture when the animal withdraws into the shell. It must not be confused with the

Valvata which is aquatic). Respiratory orifice often with a gill.

Sub-class: STREPTONEURA

Order: **Pectinibranchia:**
>Two British species; shell very winkle-like up to 1 cm. and found in and on calcareous soils, or cylindrical and glossy up to 2·5 mm., living in soil.

2. Shell reduced or well developed and spirally wound; seldom in form of a cap, never closed by an operculum. Respiratory orifice forming a lung. Hermaphrodite.

Sub-class: EUTHYNEURA

Order: **Pulmonata:**
>Breathing by a lung, freshwater or terrestrial.

>Sub-Order: **Stylommatophora** with eyes at tip of retractable tentacles.

>Sub-Order: **Basommatophora** with eyes at base of non-retractable tentacles – genus *Carychium*.

The popular division of land molluscs into slugs and snails is given here for convenience and as an aid to quick identification, but the three families of British slugs have developed from three distinct ancestral stocks and appear to have evolved parallel with each other. All slugs show a reduction of the shell and bear a general resemblance to one another externally, but the three families into which the species fall do not form a naturally related group.

There are only two species of land Pectinibranchs in the British Isles. *Pomatias elegans* (Müll.) (fig. 177) has a greyish or

epiphragm which is a covering of mucus, sometimes much calcified, which is secreted over the aperture under adverse conditions or during hibernation.

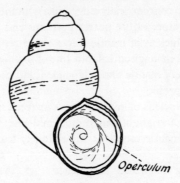

Operculum

177. *Pomatias elegans*

greyish-brown variegated shell with well-marked spiral ridges which are connected across by strong, but short ridges. The aperture is round and placed to the right of the vertical axis when viewed directly in front. The operculum is thick and calcified. Large specimens are usually females. The species occurs in limestone districts of England and Wales and is common on the Chalk. *Acme fusca* (Mont.) is a very small, pointed species living mainly in and on the surface of soil under logs and in litter. It is widespread in England; common in Ireland.

The Pulmonata are grouped here not in their natural sequence but for case in identification:

SLUGS

The chief genera and species can be identified by the following key:

(1) An external ear-shaped shell on posterior end. Live in earth and feed mainly on worms . . . genus *Testacella* (fig. 178) (three species).

(2) Mantle at anterior end of body. No external shell.

137

(a) Mantle concentrically ridged like a thumb-print (fig. 179). Respiratory orifice nearer posterior end of mantle.

(aa) Nucleus of mantle ridges above respiratory opening and in longitudinal mid-line of mantle; posterior margin of mantle obtusely angled; tail pointed when seen in profile . . genus *Limax* (figs. 176 & 179).

(bb) Nucleus of mantle ridges above respiratory opening but to right of longitudinal mid-line; posterior margin of mantle rounded; tail obliquely truncated in profile

genus *Agriolimax*

(b) Mantle roughened (shagreened) (figs. 180 & 181). Respiratory orifice near centre or near front end of mantle (figs. 180, 181)

(aa) Mantle divided by a groove into central and lateral areas (fig. 181). Respiratory orifice about central

genus *Milax*.

(bb) Mantle not divided. Respiratory orifice near front end of mantle (fig. 180) . . . genus *Arion*.

The colour of slugs is subject to some variation especially in immature specimens.

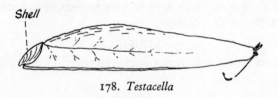

178. *Testacella*

Limax has four common species

(i) Length 9 cm. or more

L. *maximus* (L.) (fig. 176). One of the largest slugs; it has two

138

or three longitudinal darker coloured bands usually broken up into a series of spots, and the mantle is marbled with darker blotches. The tentacles are an even brown colour. The foot is uniformly pale and the pedal groove has a line of dark spots. The mucus is colourless. Generally distributed.

L. cinereo-niger (Wolf.). Also a large species, black or dark with a mid-dorsal line and prominent keel running along the latter half of the dorsum. Foot pale with lateral areas black. Tentacles spotted. Chiefly in woodlands.

L. flavus (L.). Length to about 9 cm. Tentacles a distinctive steel blue. Body yellowish-grey to green mottled with small yellow spots. Usually associated with gardens.

(ii) Length less than 9 cm.

L. marginatus (Müller). Length to about 6 cm. Colour variable grey-green; one to three continuous or broken body bands usually present and a U-shaped mark on the mantle. Readily absorbs water and becomes very translucent. Mucus clear and easily drawn into threads.

179. Mantle of *Agriolimax*   181. Mantle of *Milax*

180. Mantle of *Arion*

Agriolimax has two common species

Agriolimax reticulatus (Müller). Length to 3·5 cm. Usually yellowish-brown, rarely dark, flecked with darker markings and often appearing reticulated. Mucus milky white and sticky. Common everywhere.

A. laevis (Müller). Length to 2 cm. Chestnut brown, mantle lighter; both sparsely flecked with dark spots. Foot paler brown; mucus thin and colourless. Relatively long 'neck' when moving. Usually in marshy places.

Arion has six common species

(i) Length up to 3·5 cm.

Arion intermedius (Normand). Length to 2·5 cm. Appears 'hedgehog-like' when contracted: tubercles on body short and prominent, each ending in a point. Colour variable grey or greyish-yellow with or without bands, mantle often paler and usually with black spots at front end of pedal groove. Common and generally distributed.

A. circumscriptus (Johnston). Length up to 3·5 cm. Variable grey or greyish-yellow, bands on body and mantle, usually conspicuous, the right one arching high over the respiratory orifice. Foot opaque white; mucus white. When contracted and viewed end on, is seen to be bell-shaped, i.e. the sole is splayed out on each side. Common and widely distributed.

A. hortensis (Férussac). Length up to 3·5 cm. Not bell-shaped when contracted; foot yellow to orange. Right mantle band embraces respiratory orifice. Widely distributed; especially common in ploughed and dug land.

(ii) Length 7 cm. or more

A. subfuscus (Drap.). Length to 7 cm. Brown or yellowish-brown with distinct lateral bands at all ages. Foot yellowish-grey (not opaque white); tentacles brown with violet tinge. Widely distributed, chiefly in woods.

A. ater (L.). About 14 cm. when fully grown. Black or dark brown, less commonly grey, orange or yellow-orange. Foot with lateral areas dark grey and median area light grey. Contracts into a hemisphere and if touched will sway from side to side. Distinguishable from *A. rufus* for certain only by dissection (see figs. 182 & 183). Widely distributed.

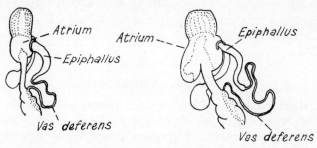

182. Genitalia of *Arion ater*   183. Genitalia of *Arion rufus*
(After Quick, 1949)

A. rufus* (L.). Similar in size to *A. ater* but usually reddish or yellowish. Foot cream coloured. Atrium with large lateral diverticulum and vas deferens one and a half times as long as the epiphallus (fig. 183). (*A. ater* has no conspicuous lateral diverticulum and the vas deferens is about as long as the epiphallus.) Widely distributed, often near gardens.

Milax has three common species

Milax gagates (Drap.). Length to 6 cm. Dark grey to black; foot pale whitish; mucus thin. Keel sharply angulated behind, darker than back. Rim of respiratory orifice dark. Generally distributed but commoner in maritime districts and the south-west of England.

* *A. rufus* is now generally regarded as a sub-species of *A. ater*.

M. sowerbyi (Férussac). Length to 7 cm. Pale brownish, sometimes mottled darker. Rim of respiratory orifice conspicuously pale. Keel not abruptly truncated and lighter in colour than the back. Foot pale; mucus yellow and sticky. Common generally, often in gardens.

M. budapestensis (Hazay). Length to 5 cm. Brownish or grey thickly speckled and lined with black; keel yellow or orange. Foot dark grey with median area darker. Mucus pale and sticky. Common and widely distributed, often in gardens.

SNAILS

(1) Aperture sinistral (on left)

Balea perversa (L.). Height 8 mm.; aperture without teeth. On trees, walls, etc.; widely distributed.

Vertigo pusilla (Müller). Height 2 mm.; aperture with several teeth. In moss, dead leaves, etc., usually in shady places, especially in the North.

There are a number of other species in this genus some of which are difficult to distinguish (see below).

Genus *Clausilia* (fig. 184). Elongated, pointed shells often ridged like a file, 8–18 mm.; aperture with several folds.

(2) Aperture dextral (on right)

(A) Height of shell greater than breadth

(i) Aperture with teeth

(a) About 2 mm. high.

Genus *Carychium* (fig. 185) (see p. 136). Aperture with three teeth; shell white and slender. On surface of earth in moss and leaves.

Genus *Vertigo*. Aperture with four to nine teeth; shell brown and plump. Mostly in damp places, under moss, by ponds, etc.

(b) About 3–4 mm. high; aperture with one tooth.

Pupilla muscorum (L.) (fig. 186). Aperture with raised brown outside rib. Mostly in open places in turf, on walls, etc.

Lauria cylindracea (da Costa) (fig. 187). Lip white and without rib. On well-drained soils in turf, under moss, on walls, etc.

(c) Height 6 mm.

Azeca goodalli (Férussac) (fig. 188). Three teeth, shell shining brown. In dead leaves, moss, turf, etc.

(d) Height 7 mm.

Abida secale (Drap.). Eight teeth; shell dull brown. In dry places, especially on calcareous soils.

(*ii*) *Aperture without teeth*

(a) Height 7 mm. or less.

Ceciliodes acicula (Müller) (fig. 189). Height 5 mm.; shell thin, shining white, very slender, rather pointed. Widely distributed, subterranean.

Columella edentula (Drap.). Height 3 mm.; shell horn-coloured, markedly cylindrical. Generally distributed in moss, leaf litter and in relatively undisturbed places.

Genus *Cochlicopa* (fig. 190). Height to 7 mm.; shell elongated oval, brown, markedly polished; lip rather darker and thicker than shell. Common at the base of herbage, in moss, under logs, etc.

(b) Height 9 mm. or more.

Cochlicella acuta (Müller) (fig. 191). Near the sea; conical, pale brown with darker band which is often broken. Height 15–25 mm. Often abundant on sea-cliffs and sand dunes.

Genus *Ena* (fig. 192). Opaque, dull brown and irregularly striated; lip white and thickened, reflexed. Height 9–15 mm. In leaf litter, moss, on rocks, trees, etc. Two species, one local, the other widespread.

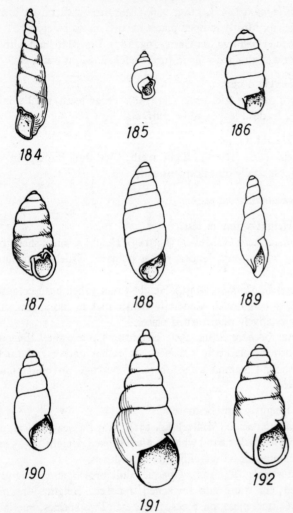

184. *Clausilia*;   185. *Carychium*;   186. *Pupilla muscorum*
187. *Lauria cylindracea*; 188. *Azeca goodalli*; 189. *Ceciliodes acicula*; 190. *Cochlicopa*; 191. *Cochlicella acuta*; 192. *Ena*

(B) Height of the shell less than breadth

(i) Shell conoid, i.e. distinctly cone shaped, and not greatly flattened. See figs. 194–200.

(a) Shell distinctly ridged, spines may be present on ridges. Genus *Acanthinula*, height 2 mm., genus *Hygromia* (see p. 148) or *Monacha granulata* (Alder) – (See p. 147).

(b) Shell smooth

(1) Shell with coloured bands, sometimes interrupted

(a) Shell 30 mm. or more high

Helix pomatia (L.). 'The Roman Snail'. Large and pale coloured with light or dark brown bands; lip whitish; about 45 mm. high when mature. Only on soils with a high calcium content; locally abundant.

H. aspersa (Müller) (fig. 193). 'The Garden Snail'. Pale brown with darker broken markings forming bands. About 32 mm. high. Common and widespread.

(b) Shell less than 30 mm.

Arianta arbustorum (L.) (fig. 194). Darkish brown with a

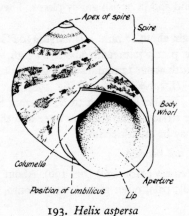

193. *Helix aspersa*

deeper coloured band (may be absent). Lip white and reflexed. Surface covered with fine spiral ridges crossed by well-marked striae. In damp places; widespread.

Helix hortensis (Müller). Very variable, pale yellow or pinkish with five or less bands which may be fused together. Lips always white and reflexed. Common.

194. *Arianta arbustorum*   195. *Helix nemoralis*

H. nemoralis (L.) (fig. 195). Similar to *H. hortensis* but lip dark coloured. Common.

Genus *Helicella*. There are four common species which live on old downland and in dryish grassy places. They are separated thus:

Conoid: height about 13 mm. – *H. virgata* (da Costa) (fig. 196).

Discoid (see p. 148); breadth about 20 mm. – *H. itala* (L.) (fig. 197); breadth about 12 mm. usually with broken or complete darker bands – *H. caperata* (Mont.) (fig. 198).

H. gigaxi (L. Pfeiffer) is similar to *H. caperata* but the spire is less raised, the striae on the shell are finer and the umbilicus is narrower; it may be almost conoid.

(2) Shell not banded

Monacha cantiana (Montagu) (fig. 199). About 12 mm. high; umbilicus small; pale, often pinkish near mouth. Common and widespread.

M. granulata (Alder). Shell about 5 mm. high, pale greyish-yellow with bristles. Common and widespread.

Pyramidula rupestris (Drap.). Shell 2 mm. high, dark brown, dull. On walls, tree-trunks, etc., usually in dryish places. Local.

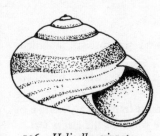

196. *Helicella virgata*

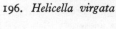

197. *Helicella itala*

198. *Helicella caperata*

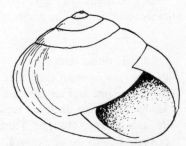

199. *Monacha cantiana*

200. *Euconulus fulvus*   201. *Vallonia*   202. *Vitrea*

Euconulus fulvus (Müller) (fig. 200). Height 2·5 mm.; brown, glossy; like a spinning-top. In moss, under stones, etc. Common.

(ii) Shell discoid, i.e. disc shaped or flattened with the breadth greater than the maximum height. See figs. 201–210.

(a) Banded – genus *Helicella* (see p.146)

(b) Not banded

   (1) Under 5 mm. broad.

Punctum pygmaeum (Drap.). Pin-head size, brown, umbilicus large. Common.

Genus *Vallonia* (fig. 201). Width 2·5 mm.; white, umbilicus half the width of the last whorl.

Genus *Vitrea* (fig. 202). Width 3 mm.; transparent, whitish or greenish; umbilicus less than half the width of the last whorl.

Genus *Retinella* (fig. 203). Width 4 mm.; brown, umbilicus slightly less than half the width of the last whorl.

   (2) Over 5 mm. broad

(a) 8 mm. broad or more

Helicogonia lapicida (L.) (fig. 204). Shell strongly keeled, brown; lip white and reflexed. In damp places, widespread.

Genus *Hygromia*. Shell not keeled or only bluntly so.

H. subrufescens (Müller). Width 9 mm.; glossy amber, shell wrinkled, umbilicus very small. In old woodland and moist habitats.

H. striolata (C. Pfeiffer) (fig. 205). Width 13 mm.; brown or horn coloured often with a pale band; the young have bristles on the shell. Common.

H. hispida (L.) (fig. 206). Width 8 mm.; brown or horn coloured, covered with bristles; often with a pale band. Common. (Young *H. hispida* are distinguishable from *H. striolata* by means of their larger umbilicus.)

Genus *Oxychilus* (fig. 207). Width to 15 mm.; glossy, shining, amber coloured and translucent.

203. *Retinella*

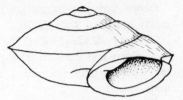

204. *Helicogonia lapicida*

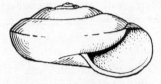

205. *Hygromia striolata*

206. *Hygromia hispida*

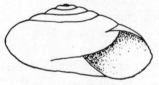

207. *Oxychilus*

208. *Zonitoides*

209. *Vitrina pellucida*

210. *Discus rotundatus*

(*b*) Up to about 8 mm. broad

Genus *Oxychilus* (fig. 207). Glossy, shining, amber coloured and translucent (see above: four species).

Retinella nitidula (Drap.) (fig. 203). Width 8 mm.; silky lustre and shining, amber coloured; very like *Oxychilus*.

Genus *Zonitoides* (fig. 208). Width 7 mm.; spire slightly raised, glossy and silky. Two species.

Vitrina pellucida (Müller) (fig. 209). Width 6 mm.; shell very thin, glossy and translucent; slightly greenish; umbilicus closed; last whorl distinctly expanded. Widespread in woodland débris, moss, etc.

Discus rotundatus (Müller) (fig. 210). Width 7–8 mm.; dull brown with darker reddish markings with strong transverse ridges; umbilicus large. Common in moss, woodland débris, etc.

REFERENCES

ELLIS, A. E. (1926) *British snails*. Oxford: Clarendon Press.

THE CONCHOLOGICAL SOCIETY OF GREAT BRITAIN AND IRELAND (1951), 'Census of the distribution of British non-marine Mollusca'. *J. Conchology*, **23**, 171–244.

JANUS, J. (1958) *Molluscs*. London: Burke.

QUICK, H. E. (1949) *Synopses of the British fauna No. 8 – Slugs. (Mollusca)*. London: Linn. Soc.

QUICK, H. E. (1960) *British slugs*. London: British Museum (Natural History).

STEP, E. (1945) *Shell life*. London: Warne.

INDEX

References to details of anatomy, methods of preservation, distribution etc., and the figures are not given here as they are readily found in the text. Numerals in heavy type refer to the main references.